The Sea Around Them

ᚦꞪE SEꓘ
ꓘꞁꝊᚒꞃꝊ ᚦꞪEꟽ

The Atlantic Ocean, A.D. 1250

VINCENT H. CASSIDY

LOUISIANA STATE UNIVERSITY PRESS
BATON ROUGE

Dedicated to the memory of
LOREN C. MACKINNEY
Mentor, guide, and friend

Preface

THIS BOOK is primarily concerned with the extent of knowledge of the North Atlantic available about A.D. 1250 in western Europe to anyone of the period interested in learning all he could about the Atlantic—its place in cosmography and in geography; the nature of such phenomena as tides, currents, and salinity; its extent; the lands which bound it, the islands within it; and what navigators, actual or imaginary, had reportedly discovered while sailing upon it. Attention is paid to the bookmen who wrote about it as well as to the boatmen who sailed its surface. No consistent attempt has been made to establish what particular manuscripts were available in particular places to particular people at particular times. However, all known sources which were in all likelihood available to thirteenth-century Europeans, in whole, in part, or in summary—extending from the time of Herodotus and Hesiod through classical antiquity and the medieval period—are reviewed, and the pertinent materials extrapolated and, when possible, interrelated.

The primary sources utilized are many and varied; the range of secondary sources is, if anything, broader. In either case discussion of a pertinent topic was justification enough for inclusion. The end result of such a policy is a non-selective bibliography in which inclusion does not constitute endorsement. Frequently materials are noted because the interpretation they offer differs from my own. In other instances, works considered suspect are cited because of nuggets of insight, or because of provocative hypotheses, or simply because appendix, addendum, or text provides access to resource materials not otherwise easily available. The author, throughout, has been guided by an awareness of a truth which J. Batalha-Reis formulated well seventy years ago in the *Geographical Journal* [IX

(1899) 210]: "Almost all the historians of geographical discoveries consider it their absolute duty to arrive at a radical conclusion in the study of problematical questions, answering with a *yes* what only deserves a *perhaps*, or, more frequently, dismissing with a *no* what ought to be held as probable."

The text and footnotes in the following pages should serve not only as an introduction to and survey of the medieval Atlantic but also as a handbook which, with the upsurge of interest in pre-Columbian contacts with America, should prove valuable to both layman and scholar.

Although the focal and, theoretically, terminal point of *The Sea Around Them* is A.D. 1250, the book summarizes and discusses earlier information concerning the ocean itself and activities upon its surface. Also, in view of current discoveries, it attempts briefly to show how the Yale Vinland map and current excavations on the North American east coast, in Northern Quebec and in Greenland, some of which pertain to a slightly later period, relate to the mid-thirteenth century.

Acknowledgments

MY INTEREST in the medieval view of the Atlantic Ocean extends over many years, and much of my scholastic life has been spent upon it. My master's thesis, under way twenty years ago, began with it; my doctoral dissertation explored it; numerous papers and articles since have probed sections of it. The following pages are a result of all the above. It is, therefore, impossible for me to list for individual thanks all the professors, colleagues, students, archivists, and reference librarians, especially those at the University of North Carolina and the University of Southwestern Louisiana, who have contributed to whatever merit this volume may have; they are legion.

I must, however, proffer specific and heart-felt thanks to Viola French of Oak Street Junior High in Derry, New Hampshire, for beginning it all; to Ivah Hackler of Pinkerton Academy for abetting my interest; to the late Loren C. MacKinney and the late Wallace E. Caldwell for their guidance and support; and to my wife for many typings and much patience; to Mathé Allain for her interest and help in research and writing during the past ten years; to Amy Page, for her aid and support during the final push; to the University of Southwestern Louisiana for facilitating my research endeavors whenever possible; to the Southeastern Institute of Medieval and Renaissance Studies for a research award grant which helped me to bring the manuscript as up to date as possible; and to Richard Wentworth, Marilyn Paul, and the staff of LSU Press for their cooperation and understanding, and the end product.

Contents

Illustrations

Introduction

No gesture is equal in futility to scratching the surface of the sea. Although many a momentary wake left by some frail ocean-borne craft has been of permanent significance to mankind, the ocean has made more of an impression upon men than they have made upon the ocean. This book deals with the impression made by the Atlantic Ocean upon the seamen who sailed it and the people who lived along its European shore before the dawn of the Modern Age. Very little will be offered which has not been discussed before by scholars in one field or another. It should be worthwhile, however, to bring the stray details together in an endeavor to determine how the people of Europe viewed the ocean—how and what they thought about it, how and why they sailed upon it.

The scope of our investigation in time and space is as broad as our subject; but, although we only scratch the surface, our course will be a charted one. We will make no attempt to present a comprehensive view of the role of the ocean in the mythologies of the various peoples met in our survey. Nor will we attempt a definitive study of real and imagined denizen of the deep, undersea flora, ship construction, and other related subjects. On the other hand, we will not avoid these when they impinge upon our study.

The present volume is intended as a cohesive, readable report which has at the same time enough of the apparatus of scholarship—including a liberal use of quotation—to serve after the first reading as a badly needed handbook. Some of our sources will be familiar; others will be generally known only to experts in rather specialized areas. When debated or debatable issues are discussed, our concern in this book will be more with delimiting the pertinent points of information than with proffering a solution. If our contributions are small, we can take comfort in marvelling with St. Basil at the minuteness of the pebbles which, collectively, encompass the sea.

If in 1250 an individual wished to learn about the Atlantic Ocean, how extensive and how accurate was the knowledge available to him? That, very briefly, is our problem. The results of our inquiry will at best approximate the answer at which such a thirteenth-century gentleman might have arrived. We will, however, attempt to make his answer and ours as nearly alike as possible. Our sources will be, in the main, those upon which he would have had to rely.

First, we shall examine the material relating to the Western Ocean, and in some cases to oceans in general, which had been accumulated by writers on diverse subjects in Greek and Roman antiquity. We want to know what the sailor discovered and what the scholar recorded; in a few exceptional cases these two are one. Our primary interest will be those works which were known, in excerpt or in entirety, to the medieval reader.

Next we shall follow the Christian scholar through the early Middle Ages in an attempt to determine what he kept of his classical heritage, what he added to it, and what his conscience or predisposition found necessary to amend. Some amendment would be called for to assure conformity with the Bible and with the doctrinal pronouncements of the Church Fathers.

We shall then concern ourselves with the actual ventures upon the Atlantic by northern Europeans—who sailed, why and where they sailed, and what they sailed in. We will attempt to determine the limits of navigation and the extent to which the body of traditional knowledge was augmented by the personal observations of medieval pilgrims, travelers, merchants, and sailors.

After examining the literary or cartographical works of the period 1000 to 1250 which were in some way concerned with the Atlantic Ocean, we should be in a position to summarize the geographical concepts pertaining to the Atlantic Ocean which existed in the mid-thirteenth century. John Kirtland Wright, whose knowledge of geographical lore qualifies him to serve as one of our guides, reminds us:

When viewed historically, geographical concepts are seen to have come from an immense variety of sources. They have sprung partly from activities that cause men to travel over the surface of the earth: war, commerce, pilgrimage, diplomacy, pleasure. They have also sprung from the accumulated learning and lore of preceding ages and to no small extent from unfettered flights of the imagination.[1]

Hail and fair warning.

VINCENT H. CASSIDY

Lafayette, Louisiana
August 15, 1967

---

[1] John Kirtland Wright, *Geographical Lore of the Time of the Crusades* (New York, 1924), xix.

The Sea Around Them

I *Beyond the Pillars of Heracles*

TLAS, the mythological Titan, was reputed to know the depth of every sea. Condemned by Zeus to stand on the western fringe of the world with the weight of the sky upon his shoulders, he would at least have known the depth of the water in which he was standing. In his more mobile youth Atlas had married Pleione, the daughter of Ocean. By her he had seven daughters, the Pleiades, two of whom were seduced by the sea-god Poseidon.[1] Atlas therefore was not only physically but personally involved with the oceanic west. As a result the classic Mediterranean world referred to the ocean which lay beyond Gibraltar as the Sea of Atlas, or the Atlantic.

The first surviving instance of the use of the term Atlantic in reference to that ocean is found in the writing of the Greek historian Herodotus.[2] Long before Herodotus, however, the Atlantic, by whatever name, was known about and sailed upon. Stone Age fishermen probed the oceanic deeps.[3] Stone Age architects, who left such monuments as Stonehenge along the Atlantic seaboard, were seafarers, even transporting much of their stone by water.[4]

[1] Homer, *Odyssey*, I, 51–54, trans. A. T. Murray (New York, 1919); Hesiod, *Theogony*, 517–20, in Hesiod, *The Homeric Hymns and Homerica*, trans. H. G. Eveleyn-White (New York, 1936); Apollodorus, *The Library*, III, i, trans. James G. Frazer (New York, 1921).

[2] Herodotus, *History*, I, 203, trans. A. D. Godley (New York, 1920). Cf. Diodorus Siculus, *Historical Library*, III, 60, trans. C. H. Oldfather (Cambridge, Mass., 1935).

[3] For a summary of the archaeological evidence for ancient European seafaring craft, see Stuart Piggott, *Ancient Europe From the Beginnings of Agriculture to Classical Antiquity* (Chicago, 1965), 144–45, 165, 187, 211. Re Phoenician shipbuilding, see also Auguste Toussaint, *History of the Indian Ocean*, trans. Guicharnaud (London, 1961), 23.

[4] Gerald S. Hawkins, *Stonehenge Decoded* (New York, 1965), 63–66. See also Sir John Clapham, *A Concise Economic History of Britain From the Earliest Times to 1750* (London, 1949), 5–7.

Later in the mists of protohistory, Minoan and Mycenaean merchants entered the Atlantic from the Mediterranean. These traders were followed by seamen from the Phoenician cities of Tyre and Sidon in search of dye-stuffs, amber, and tin.

On the Atlantic coast of the Iberian peninsula was the mysterious flourishing commercial outpost Tartessus, the actual site of which still eludes archaeologists, but whose ships may have been ancestral to fishing vessels found today on the coast of Portugal. Herodotus tells of Colaeus of Samos, a Greek merchant who was driven by storm through the Straits of Gibraltar to the port of Tartessus.[5] Colaeus sold his entire cargo at Tartessus, and his success inspired others. The Greek colony Massilia, in what is today southern France, carried on trade with Tartessus, and possibly the Atlantic coast beyond, until Carthage managed to close the straits to the Greeks. Tartessus then faded away, undoubtedly with Carthaginian help, and Gades, modern Cadiz, became the chief port in the area.

In addition to trade, the Phoenicians and Carthaginians found other enticements offered by the Atlantic. Archil, a lichen which yielded precious violet dye, abounded on some of the islands. There were also fish to be caught. Some fishing boats remained so long at sea or fished so far out that it was necessary to salt down catches.[6]

When the power of Carthage was at its height, a Punic admiral named Hanno reputedly made a voyage down the West African coast.[7] He appears to have sailed to within 8° of the equator and to have established settlements on the way. An account attributed to Hanno says that he took thirty thousand settlers with him on his expedition.[8]

---

[5] Herodotus, *History*, IV, 152.

[6] Aristotle (pseudo), *De Mirabilibus Auscultationibus*, 136, trans. L. D. Dowdall (Oxford, 1909).

[7] Pliny the Elder, *Natural History*, II, 67; V, 1; VI, 36, trans. H. Rackham (Cambridge, Mass., 1942).

[8] Hanno, *The Periplus of Hanno*, trans. Wilfred H. Schoff (Philadelphia, 1912), 3–5. For a unique interpretation cf. Leo Frobenius, *The Voice of Africa* (London, 1913), I, 338–39: "It was a sort of guide book, another kind of ancient Baedeker for traders, colonizers, etc. . . . 'Hanno' . . . was

About the time that Hanno was exploring the African coast, a fellow countryman, Himilco, was traveling northward to explore the remoter shores of Europe.[9] He may have been in search of the Tartessan source of tin. The account of his voyage is nebulously preserved in the works of ancient authors. The *Ora Maritima* of Avienus attributed a horrendous description of the Atlantic to him. Himilco, Avienus said, reported that it took four months to reach his destination, that there was no breeze to propel the ship, that the ocean was sluggish, and that the seaweed was so thick it often held the ship back.[10] Avienus wrote that the sea to westward was even worse, the ocean in that direction being boundless and not navigable because of continual fog and darkness. Moreover, the entire sea was filled with monsters.[11] Himilco's report of immense quantities of algae which obstructed his ship's passage has frequently been cited as proof of familiarity with the "Sargasso Sea," but, since he was exaggerating in any case, he may have been grossly exaggerating conditions closer to home.[12]

Himilco may actually have been responsible for the exaggerated account of the hazards awaiting those who would sail the Atlantic. The Carthaginians were not above practicing deception in order to preserve their monopoly. The Greek geographer Strabo related that the Carthaginians would even sacrifice their own ships in order to destroy ships following them rather than reveal a secret trade route.[13]

Auguste Toussaint, in his *History of the Indian Ocean*, refers to the secret routes of the Phoenicians, and their Carthaginian

---

as much a generic name on Carthaginian lips of that old time as 'Jack-tar' is on ours."

Euthymenes of Massilia may have preceded Hanno down the African coast, but he is an even more shadowy figure. For extant sources and discussion, see Richard Hennig, *Terrae Incognitae* (Leiden, 1944), I, 80–85.

[9] Pliny, *Natural History*, II, 67. Pliny elsewhere may be naming another early explorer of whom nothing else is known. Cf. *ibid.*, VII, 56: "Tin was first imported by Midacritus from the island of Cassiteris."

[10] Avienus, *Ora Maritima*, 113–29, ed. A. Berthelot (Paris, 1934).

[11] *Ibid.*, 380–89, 406–13.

[12] See J. Oliver Thomson, *History of Ancient Geography* (London, 1948), 54–55.

[13] Strabo, *Geography*, III, 5, xi, trans. H. L. Jones, (New York, 1923).

descendants in the Atlantic. He concludes: "All that we know of the Phoenicians leads us to believe that the obscurity which now covers their maritime activities was deliberate."[14]

Herodotus wrote in his history that Phoenicians in the service of Necho II of Egypt, c. 600 B.C., successfully circumnavigated Africa, sailing down the east coast and up the west. He also reported an unsuccessful attempt by Persians to do the same.[15] The only other recorded attempts at such a voyage in antiquity were those of the Greek navigator Eudoxus of Cyzicus. His first attempt failed, and he tried again. The second time he may have met with foul play at the hands of the Carthaginians, as Carthage jealously guarded her monopoly of Atlantic trade until she bowed to Rome at the end of the Second Punic War.[16]

Stray references in the odes of Pindar (c. 511–443 B.C.) seem to show the effect of Carthaginian propaganda upon the Mediterranean world. Pindar warned his listeners that neither the wise nor the unwise might fare beyond the pillars of Heracles.[17] In another passage he cautioned that no one should sail from Gades westward.[18]

The Carthaginian blockade was not effective enough to prohibit the voyage of the Massilian mariner and scientist Pytheas. About the time that Alexander the Great was rending the Persian curtain of empire, Pytheas set out somewhat more reservedly to probe the northern ocean. He apparently sailed through the pillars of Heracles[19] and then northward on a voyage of exploration, al-

[14] Toussaint, *Indian Ocean*, 23.

[15] Herodotus, *History*, IV, 42–43. The Phoenicians reported that when rounding the tip, the sun was to their left.

[16] Strabo, *Geography*, II, 3, iv–v. Cf. Pomponius Mela, *De Chorographia*, III, 9, ed. Karl Frick (Leipzig, 1880); Pliny, *Natural History*, II, 67. Arrian in *Anabasis of Alexander*, IV, 7, v, trans. E. Iliff Robson (New York, 1933), says that Alexander the Great contemplated such a voyage.

[17] Pindar, *Olympian Odes*, III, 43–45, in Pindar, *Odes*, trans. Sir John Sandys (New York, 1924).

[18] Pindar, *Nemean Odes*, IV, 69–70.

[19] This term for the Straits of Gibraltar has the following mythological interpretation, supplied by Apollodorus, *The Library*, II, 5, x: "[Heracles] . . . erected as tokens of his journey two pillars over against each other at the boundaries of Europe and Libya." Apollodorus adds that Heracles, annoyed by the Sun's heat, "bent his bow at the god, who in admiration

though such a voyage might have been undertaken after crossing Gaul by land. He is thought to have reached Britain and sailed beyond it for six days, finally reaching Thule. How Pytheas eluded the Carthaginian blockade is a matter of some debate, but no one questions that he did. Thule is a problem. Where was it located and what exactly did Pytheas find there? These are questions that scholars have asked themselves with only a modicum of success from Pytheas' day to our own.[20]

Thule was not the only island reported to exist well out in the Atlantic. There were the famous Hesperides with groves of trees producing golden apples, as well as the marvelous Fortunate Islands. According to the *Odyssey*, the Elysian Fields were in the west, either surrounded or bordered by ocean. Hesiod and Pindar concurred; heroes abounding in courage and lacking in iniquity found their immortal haven "where the ocean breezes blow around the Islands of the Blest." [21]

The Phoenicians probably discovered the Canary and Madeira island groups. Their Carthaginian successors were certainly aware of them.[22] The Carthaginians also may have left vestige, in the form of coinage, of at least one visit to the Azores in the fourth century B.C.[23] When rumors of such Phoenician and Carthaginian

---

of his hardihood, gave him a golden goblet in which he crossed the ocean."

Heracles was frequently regarded as the patron of merchants, and natural landmarks which were of benefit to seafarers were frequently attributed to him.

[20] For a tentative account of the voyage of Pytheas, see Vilhjalmur Stefansson, *Ultima Thule* (New York, 1940), 1–107. See also Hennig, *Terrae Incognitae*, I, 155–82; Fridtjof Nansen, *In Northern Mists* (London, 1911), I, 43–73; M. Cary and E. H. Warmington, *The Ancient Explorers* (London, 1929), 33–40; and Antonio Ballesteros (ed.), *Genesis del Descubrimiento*, in *Historia de América* (Buenos Aires, 1947), III, 58–66. For the Greek sources concerning Pytheas, see E. H. Warmington, *Greek Geography* (New York, 1934), 169–76. For this author's views, see Vincent Cassidy, "Voyage of an Island," *Speculum*, XXXVIII (1963), 595–602.

[21] Homer, *Odyssey*, IV, 561–65; Hesiod, *Works and Days*, 167–72; Pindar, *Olympic Odes*, II, 68–76.

[22] Diodorus Siculus, *Historical Library*, V, 19, 20; Aristotle (pseudo), *De Mirabilibus Auscultationibus*, 84–85. Cf. Hennig, *Terrae Incognitae*, I, 40–50; Cary and Warmington, *The Ancient Explorers*, 53.

[23] Hennig, *Terrae Incognitae*, I, 138–40.

discoveries reached Greek ears, identification of these islands with the Islands of the Blest followed naturally.

During the Roman period there were some attempts at exploration in the Atlantic beyond the Roman world to the west and south. Pliny the Elder reported that "Scipio Aemilianus during his command in Africa placed a fleet of vessels at the service of the historian Polybius for the purpose of making a voyage of discovery in that part of the world.[24]

Unfortunately, it is not clear from Pliny how far down the African coast Polybius got, and there is no other extant account. Juba II, the remarkable savant king of Mauretania, sent an expedition down the northwest coast of Africa to explore the Canaries. Pliny also credited Juba with occupying the "Purple Islands," where he established a dye industry, but the Roman author's description does not enable us to identify them. The surviving text (which may be more at fault than Pliny himself) says that, to reach the Canaries from the Purple Islands, one must sail 625 miles, first for 225 miles due west, and then 375 toward the east.[25] Someone was horribly confused.

Plutarch reported that the Roman general Sertorius, while on the Atlantic coast of Spain, "fell in with some sailors" who had recently come back from some Atlantic islands about 1,100 miles from Africa. They were called the Islands of the Blest. The sailors reported that these islands "not only have a rich soil which is excellent for plowing and planting, but also produce a natural fruit that is plentiful and wholesome enough to feed without toil or trouble, a leisure folk." Moreover, they added, "an air that is salubrious, owing to the climate and the moderate changes in the seasons, prevails on the islands. . . . Therefore a firm belief has made its way, even to the Barbarians, that here is the Elysian Field and the abode of the blessed, of which Homer sang." [26] Sertorius, when he heard of these islands, wished to go there "and live in quiet, freed from tyranny and wars that would never end." [27] Circumstances, and his

---

[24] Pliny, *Natural History*, V, 1; VI, 36.

[25] *Ibid.*, VI, 36–37.

[26] Plutarch, *Sertorius*, 8, in Plutarch, *Lives*, trans. Bernadotte Perrin (New York, 1919).

[27] *Ibid.*, 9.

assassination in 72 B.C., kept this plan from fruition.[28] However, he was then eligible for permanent residency on the Islands of the Blest.

After the establishment of Roman rule, except for occasional plagues of piracy, commerce was unhampered, and Mediterranean merchants sailed up and down the Atlantic coast. As the Roman world expanded, other avenues of knowledge were opened; Britain and to a lesser extent Ireland became well known. Much of Britain became a part of the Roman Empire.

Many Romans had a traditional distrust of the sea and seafaring. The poet Catullus seemed to have a genuine fondness for the sea.[29] However, it is frequently pointed out that, in most things, he was the most non-Roman of Romans. Horace was most disapproving: "In vain did heaven's care dissever land from land by ocean's churlish flood, if yet those godless ships bound madly in contempt o'er channels not allowed." [30]

In 12 B.C. Drusus Germanicus, the stepson of Augustus, sailed along the Frisian coast and, sometime before his death in 9 B.C., he captured some offshore islands.[31] Suetonius acclaimed him as the first Roman general to sail the northern ocean.[32]

In his official autobiography, Augustus himself boasted that in A.D. 5 his fleet had sailed "through the ocean from the mouth of the Rhine toward the region of the rising sun as far as the lands of the Cimbri to which before that time no Roman had penetrated either by land or sea." [33]

In A.D. 16 another Drusus Germanicus, a son of the earlier general, ventured seaward. The younger Germanicus assembled one

[28] For another allusion to Sertorius and the Fortunate Isles, see Lucius Annaeus Florus, *Epitome Rerum Romanum*, II, 10, trans. E. S. Forster (New York, 1929).

[29] Mona P. Hodnett, "The Sea in Roman Poetry," *Classical Journal*, XV (1919–20), 67–82.

[30] Horace, *Ode III*, in *Poems*, trans. A. H. Bryce (London, 1907).

[31] Strabo, *Geography*, VII, 1, iii; Dio Cassius, *Roman History*, LIV, 32, trans. Ernest Cary (New York, 1916).

[32] Suetonius, *Claudius*, 1, in *Lives of the Caesars*, trans. J. C. Rolfe (New York, 1920).

[33] Augustus, *Res Gestae Divi Augusti*, 26, ed. Jean Gagé (Paris, 1935). This author's translation. Cf. Pliny, *Natural History*, II, 67; Paterculus, *Compendium of Roman History*, II, 106, trans. Frederick W. Shipley (New York, 1924)

thousand ships for troop movement in the North Sea. The fleet, with soldiers aboard, moved down the Ems and into the North Sea. Then disaster struck. A great storm scattered the fleet and took a grim toll of men, ships, and equipment.[34]

The expedition of the younger Germanicus is noteworthy for several reasons. That the North Sea should at the decision of a Roman commander be "troubled by the sound and impulse of the sails and oars of a thousand ships" indicates a large naval potential. Such a conclusion is reinforced by the fact that ships crippled by the storm which made their way to port could be "instantly refitted." [35] Moreover, it is possible that this same Roman commander was involved in an attempt at exploration.

In Tacitus' *Germania* the following curious passage appears:

Nay, in that quarter we have essayed the ocean itself, and beyond our range rumour has published the existence of pillars of Hercules; whether it be that Hercules visited those shores, or because we have agreed to enter all marvels everywhere to his credit. Nor did Drusus Germanicus lack audacity, but Ocean vetoes inquiry alike touching itself and touching Hercules; and soon the attempt was abandoned, and it was voted more religious and more reverent to believe in the works of Deity than to comprehend them.[36]

Many commentators upon the text think that Tacitus is referring to the voyage of the elder Germanicus in 12 B.C. but nothing we know of that voyage explains Tacitus' statement. The disastrous troop movement of the younger Germanicus fits better, but here, too, there are difficulties. The reference is not to troop movements, but rather to a voyage of exploration: "We have essayed (*temptavimus*) the ocean itself." The object of the voyage seems to have been shores some distance away which had been, at least traditionally, formerly visited by Hercules. The voyage was ambitious but not successful because the "Ocean vetoed inquiry" and "the attempt was abandoned."

There is another piece of the puzzle which adds to but does not complete the picture. The *Suasoriae* of M. Annaeus Seneca (c. A.D.

[34] Tacitus, *Annals*, II, 23–24, trans. John Jackson (New York, 1931).
[35] *Ibid.*, II, 23–24.
[36] Tacitus, *Germania*, 34, in *Dialogus; Agricola; Germania*, trans. William Peterson (New York, 1914).

37) contained a fragment of a poem by Pedo Albinovanus, who is presumed to have been serving under the younger Germanicus in A.D. 15 when "the prefect Pedo led the cavalry along the Frisian frontier." [37] This poetic fragment concerned a "voyage of Germanicus" in the northern ocean. The younger Germanicus appears the one involved. Although the poem is usually equated with his unfortunate troop movements in 16 A.D., it, too, seems to be describing an attempted voyage of exploration.

Already long behind them they have seen the daylight and the sun fade away, already banished from the boundaries of the known world, boldly through the forbidden darkness they go to the limit of things and the outermost shores of the world. Now they see that Ocean, which contains enormous monsters beneath its waves, which contains on all sides fierce whales and seals, itself surge up grasping the ships. The noise of the sea itself increases, and terror. Already they imagine the fleet deserted by the strong winds, and the ships sticking in the sludge, and themselves even now abandoned by unswerving fate to be mangled by sea monsters in a cruel end. And the one, who above on the high prow struggles with valiant visage to penetrate the gloomy atmosphere, unable to distinguish anything in this forsaken world, pours words such as these from his tormented breast: "Where are we going? The day itself flees and ultimate nature encompasses an abandoned world with perpetual gloom. Are we seeking people located on the other side under a different pole of the heavens, and for an unknown world free from the blast of winds? The gods call us back and they forbid mortal eyes to see the boundary of things. Why do we violate strange seas and sacred waters with our oars; for what reason disturb the peaceful abode of the gods?" [38]

---

[37] Tacitus, *Annals*, I, 60.

[38] M. Annaeus Seneca, *Suasoriae*, I, 15, in *Oratorum et Rhetorum of Seneca the Elder*, ed. H. J. Müller (Leipzig, 1887). This author's translation. The original, without concern for line breaks, is:

. . . quanto Pedo, qui in navigante Germanico dicit: "iam pridem post terga diem solemque relictum iamque vident, notis extorres finibus orbis per non concessas audaces ire tenebras ad rerum metas extremaque litora mundi, nunc illum, pigris immania monstra sub undis qui ferat, Oceanum, qui saevas undique pristis aequoreosque canes, ratibus consurgere prensis. accumulat fragor ipse metus. iam sidere limo navigia et rapido desertam flamine classem seque feris credunt per inertia fata marinis iam non felici laniandos sorte relinqui. atque aliquis prora caecum sublimis ab alta aera pugnaci luctatus rumpere visu, ut nihil erepto valuit dinoscere mundo, obstructa in

There is hardly room for doubt that the fragment of Pedo's poem described the voyage to which Tacitus referred in his *Germania*.[39] These people were certainly "essaying" the sea, apparently rather far to the north, and the ocean seems to be "vetoing inquiry." Unfortunately there appears to be no other direct evidence. We will have occasion to recall some passages in the poem again. For the present it will suffice to show that even "official" Romans were occasionally interested in probing the unknown.

Elsewhere Tacitus noted that in A.D. 84 under Agricola the Roman fleet sailed northward and for the first time rounded the north coast of Britain. The "shores of Thule even were descried." Tacitus added: "However, they brought the report that the sea was sluggish and heavy . . . I presume because land and mountain, the cause and occasion of storms, are fewer and further between, and because the deep mass of uninterrupted water is slower to set in motion." [40]

There is another item concerning Roman exploration in the north which proves nothing but may indicate a great deal—the recent discovery in Iceland of coins from the reigns of Probus (276–82), Aurelianus (270–75), and Diocletian (284–305).[41] Someone, at some time, brought them there.

------

talis effundit pectora voces: quo ferimur? fugit ipse dies orbemque relictum ultima perpetuis claudit natura tenebris. anne alio positas ultra sub cardine gentes atque alium flabris intactum quaerimus orbem? di revocant rerumque vetant cognoscere finem mortales oculos: aliena quid aequora remis et sacras violamus aquas divumque quietas turbamus sedes?"

[39] Nansen, *In Northern Mists*, I, 82–85, discusses the poem and the problem of Germanicus very competently. However, he does not mention the quotation from Tacitus' *Germania* which to this investigator seems intimately concerned.

[40] Tacitus, *Agricola*, 10. In this connection, either Tacitus is exaggerating or he considered Thule to be one of the Shetlands. See Harry E. Burton, *Discovery of the Ancient World* (Cambridge, 1932), 82–83.

[41] Stefan Einarsson, "Bjolfur and Grendill in Iceland," *Modern Language Notes*, LXXI (1956), 81. See also T. C. Lethbridge, *Herdsmen and Hermits* (Cambridge, 1950), 55; Geoffrey Ashe, *Land to the West* (New York, 1962), 128; and Archibald R. Lewis, *In Northern Seas* (Princeton, 1958), 34 n.

By the fourth century A.D., piracy had become a most serious problem in the north, and a fleet was maintained in Britain in a vain effort to suppress it. Another official interest in the Atlantic developed at that same time when the manufacture of purple cloth became a monopoly of the government. This monopoly was extended to include control of the fishermen (*murileguli*) who gathered shellfish which produced the dye.[42]

Dicuil, an Irish monk writing in the ninth century, made tantalizing reference to another official project which may have been concerned with the Atlantic: "Ever since I composed a pamphlet on ten questions concerning the art of grammar, I have thought a book should follow concerning the extent of the earth's regions, according to the authority of those whom the holy Emperor Theodosius sent to measure those regions." [43] Dicuil, however, says nothing definite about this expedition (or expeditions), other than that it occurred in the fifteenth year of Theodosius' reign, and neither does anyone else. Nor is it known which Emperor Theodosius Dicuil saw fit to characterize as "holy." Probability, if not history, favors Theodosius I, the Great.[44]

There were many others in antiquity who sailed upon the sea, but in most cases their names and their memories have disappeared

---

[42] Arthur E. R. Boak, *Manpower Shortage and the Fall of the Roman Empire in the West* (Ann Arbor, 1955), 104–105. See also Lewis, *In Northern Seas*, 5–6.

[43] Dicuil, *De Mensura Orbis Terrae*, Prologus I, ed. G. Parthey (Berlin, 1870). This author's translation.

[44] Dicuil, *De Mensura*, I, 1: "Jn quinto-decimo anno regni imperatoris Theodosii praecepit ille suis missis provintias orbis terrae in longitudinem et latitudiem mensurari."

The date of this mission was, therefore, c. A.D. 393 or 422. Cf. Stefansson, *Ultima Thule*, 60 ". . . since Dicuil refers to 'Saint' or 'holy' Theodosius it would appear that the Emperor Theodosius III, who ended his life in a monastery as an ordained priest and who was famed for miracles, might also enter into the picture, if we suppose that he could have undertaken such a survey in his brief reign of only about a year, 716–718." It would seem that, in this case, Stefansson had not paid enough attention to his sources. See Hennig, *Terrae Incognitae*, II, 18–21, for a discussion of this problem.

as completely as the wakes of the ships. As always, the contribution of the nameless, faceless mass is as immense as it is immeasurable.[45]

---

[45] Although we will have little need or occasion to cite Leonard Outhwaite, *The Atlantic, A History of an Ocean* (New York, 1957), his emphasis differs from our own and the general reader might be interested in his survey of the pre-Columbian Atlantic (pp. 73–131). In this connection we might also recommend the opening chapters in Pierre de Latil and Jean Rivoire, *Man and the Underwater World* (New York, 1956) and Geoffrey Ashe, *Land to the West*. For more on navigation in the ancient world, consult Eva G. R. Taylor, *The Haven-finding Art* (London, 1956); and Walter Woodburn Hyde, *Ancient Greek Mariners* (New York, 1947). One should acknowledge Charles H. Hapgood, *Maps of the Ancient Sea Kings* (New York, 1966), which suggests that a map produced by Piri Re'is, a Turkish admiral, in 1513 had Carthaginian and Alexandrian maps among its prototypes.

II *Off the Deep End*

OUR KNOWLEDGE of the exploits of the men who sailed the seas usually is based upon what other men recorded. In each century the scholar derived his knowledge of the Atlantic Ocean from earlier writers and added to it from his own experience and that of his contemporaries. His view of the ocean was modified by his concept of the world. Such a cosmography might be based upon the teachings of earlier theorists or upon his own excursions into the realm of pure thought.

Much that we know about early concepts of the Atlantic Ocean comes from material incidental to the author's purpose. Homer, for example, is one of our oldest sources. As Hyde points out in his *Ancient Greek Mariners*, much of the *Odyssey* is based on sea lore, some derived from accounts of Phoenician and Cretan voyages and some based on even earlier Indo-European folklore.[1]

The Homeric idea of the earth as a flat disk floating in or surrounded by water was accepted by many. Some men, however, at least from the sixth century before Christ, believed the earth to be spherical. Diogenes Laertius, an ancient picker of great minds, said that the first person who asserted that the earth was of a spherical form was the Greek philosopher Parmenides.[2] He reported that Anaximander also believed the earth to be a sphere,[3] and that Pythagoras not only believed the earth to be spherical but taught "that there are antipodes, and that what is below, as respects us, is above in respect of them." [4]

---

[1] Hyde, *Ancient Greek Mariners*, 72.

[2] Diogenes Laertius, *Parmenides*, II, in *Lives and Opinions of Eminent Philosophers*, trans. C. D. Yonge (London, 1853). See also Lloyd A. Brown, *The Story of Maps* (Boston, 1949), 22–33.

[3] Diogenes Laertius, *Anaximander*, II, in *Eminent Philosophers*.

[4] Diogenes Laertius, *Pythagoras*, XIX, in *Eminent Philosophers*.

Aristotle in *De Caelo* stated that the earth was not only circular in shape, but was also "a sphere of no great size." [5] According to the Greek philosopher, physical law required a spherical earth and observation proved this to be true. All heavy bodies were attracted to the center of the universe, and Aristotle's universe was earth-centered. He proved to his own satisfaction that the ocean formed the surface of a sphere in the following way:

... [T]he surface of water is seen to be spherical if we take as our starting-point the fact that water naturally tends to collect in a hollow place—"hollow" meaning "nearer the centre." Draw from the centre the lines AB, AC, and let their extremities be joined by the straight line BC. The line AD drawn to the base of the triangle, will be shorter than either of the radii. Therefore the place in which it terminates will be a hollow place. The water then will collect there until equality is established, that is until the line AE is equal to the two radii. Thus water forces its way to the ends of the radii, and there only will it rest: but the line which connects the extremities of the radii is circular: therefore the surface of the water BEC is spherical. [6]

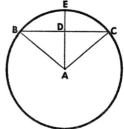

Visible proof of the spherical nature of the earth was to be found in the earth's shadow upon the moon, argued Aristotle. Furthermore, some constellations were visible in one place and not in another, which could not be the case if the earth were flat. From the time of Aristotle, the sphericity of the earth became generally accepted by the educated, and such classical geographers and astronomers as Hyginus offered it to the Middle Ages. [7]

Pliny the Elder, the Roman encyclopedist of natural history, would also assure medieval scholars that the earth was spherical. According to his "physical law," the earth radiated outward from its center, "the ceaseless revolution of the world around her forcing her immense globe into the shape of a sphere." Pliny noted that people at any point on the earth's surface could stand with their feet toward its center. "Here," he sighed, "there is a mighty

[5] Aristotle, *De Caelo*, II, 14, trans. J. L. Stocks (Oxford, 1922).
[6] *Ibid.*, II, 4.
[7] Hyginus, *Poeticon Astronomicon*, I–VIII, in *Auctores Mythographi Latini*, ed. Augustin Van Staveren (Amstelaed, 1742).

battle between learning on one side and the common herd on the other." [8] (This "mighty battle" was just a preliminary skirmish. A mightier battle was soon to follow when many learned men would be religiously inspired to join forces with "the common herd" upon this issue.) Pliny offered an intermediate theory, acceptable, he said, even to the unlearned—that of an earth formed like a pine cone and inhabited all round. Exactly why this was more acceptable was, Pliny assumed, obvious to his readers.

What about the surface of the ocean? Was it, too, part of a spherical surface? Pliny acknowledged that "what the crowd most debates is if it must believe that the conformation of the waters also rises in a curve." He continued:

Nevertheless nothing else in the natural world is more visibly manifest. For (1) hanging drops of liquid always take the shape of small round globes; (2) when dropped on dust . . . they are seen to be absolutely spherical; (3) in goblets when filled the surface curves upward most at the centre . . . though this is more easily discovered by theory than by observation; and (4) . . . when weighty solids are put into [a full cup] . . . these pass inside the liquid and raise its surface to a peak. . . . (5) The same cause explains why the land is not visible from the deck of a ship when in sight from the masthead; and why as a vessel passes far into the distance . . . it appears slowly to sink. . . . Lastly (6) what other conformation could have caused the ocean which we acknowledge to be at the extreme outside, to cohere and not fall away, if there is no boundary beyond to enclose it? [9]

Pliny then turned from visible manifestations to theory. He presented the arguments of Aristotle and "the Greek investigators, [who] greatly to their delight and to their glory, prove by subtle mathematical reasoning" that the ocean formed part of a spherical surface.[10]

The Homeric view of the earth as a land mass surrounded by the river ocean had to be modified, but not drastically, to adjust to sphericity.[11] The other side of the river might simply become the

[8] Pliny, *Natural History*, II, 64–65.
[9] *Ibid.*
[10] *Ibid.*
[11] Except in pure poetry. Cf. Horace, *Epodes*, XVI, trans. A. H. Bryce (London, 1907): "The ocean stream that girds the world awaits us: let's seek the lands, the happy lands, those islands of the blest."

other side of the earth, though the river would then become somewhat swollen in its proportions.

Sphericity became generally accepted among the learned, but
the size of the sphere remained a matter of some debate. Aristotle,
as noted, held that the earth was "a sphere of no great size." Eratosthenes' estimate of 252,000 stades for the circumference of the
earth was apparently very close. This seems to represent 24,662
miles as compared to the true measure of 24,587. There is, however, some question as to the length of Eratosthenes' stade.[12]

A distinction was generally drawn between the total area of the
earth, the *ge*, and the *oikumene*, or known inhabited land mass. The
Socrates of the *Phaedo* expressed his conviction "that the earth is
a round body in the centre of the heavens." He then added: "Also
I believe that the earth is very vast, and that we who dwell in the
region extending from the river Phasis to the Pillars of Heracles
inhabit a small portion only about the sea, like ants or frogs about
a marsh, and that there are other inhabitants of many other like
places . . . everywhere on the face of the earth. . . ." [13]

Many, especially those with a penchant for science fiction, took
advantage of a possible vast expanse of ocean and the lack of
definite knowledge to postulate land masses of their own design
and to populate these with inhabitants as weird as fancies are.
Typical is Lucian's description, in *A True Story*, of a transatlantic
voyage which aimed to "find out what formed the farther border
of the ocean and what peoples lived there." According to his tale,
more than eight days after leaving the Mediterranean the storm-
tossed ship reached a hilly forested island. Here, Lucian reported:
"We had advanced about a third of a mile through thick forest
when we came upon a bronze shaft. It was inscribed in Greek,
and the legend, dim and worn, read: 'This marks the spot reached
by Heracles and Dionysus.' And pressed in the rock nearby, were
two sets of footprints, one a hundred feet long, the other somewhat less." After deciding that the larger footprint was that of
Heracles, the explorers pushed on to a river "not of water, but of

---

[12] Cf. Thomson, *History of Ancient Geography*, 162.

[13] Plato, *Phaedo*, 109, in *Dialogues*, trans. Benjamin Jowett (Chicago,
1952), 247.

wine, which had the very same taste as our vintage Chian." Later they came upon "vines of a fabulous type. The part growing out of the ground, the stalk proper, was well set up and thick. But the part above that was a perfect replica of a female body from hips to head, [with] branches bearing clusters of grapes growing out of the tips of their fingers and, instead of hair, actual shoots with leaves and grapes." These creatures welcomed the strangers, "some in Lydian, some in Indian, but most in Greek. They also started kissing us on the lips, and everyone they did this to immediately became drunk and began to reel." [14]

On the more serious side, the Pythagorean concept of the antipodal land masses was popularized by Crates of Mallus (c. 145 B.C.) whose hypothesized Australian continent was increasingly accepted during the next several centuries. Also generally accepted was the observation of Eratosthenes (c. 225 B.C.) that the world was divided into five zones: a central torrid zone, two temperate zones, and two frigid zones. Crates also hypothesized two other land masses, one northern and one southern, on the opposite side of the globe, but these were not generally accepted.[15]

These concepts were often reflected in classical literature. Virgil in his *Georgics* referred to the five zones and the antipodes.[16] Cicero, in writing *On the Commonwealth*, included the following in the section called the "Dream of Scipio:"

You perceive, moreover, that the earth is also adorned and encircled with what we may call girdles. Two of these zones are exactly opposite to one another and, lying beneath the very poles of the heavens, are congealed with ice. On the other hand, the middle zone which is the largest, is parched by the sun's heat. Two are habitable, and of these the southern zone, in which the inhabitants are your antipodes, touches you not at all. There remains then, the northern zone in which you

[14] Lucian, *A True Story*, 5–8, in *Selected Satires of Lucian*, ed. and trans. Lionel Casson (Chicago, 1962), 15–17. Lucian also included a moon voyage. A similar story had been told earlier by Antonius Diogenes. See Thomson, *History of Ancient Geography*, 238; Lucian, *Works*, ed. and trans. A. M. Harmon (Cambridge, Mass., 1961) I, 261 n.

[15] Strabo, *Geography*, I, 4; II, 5, x; VI.

[16] Virgil, *Georgics*, I, 231–58, in *Opera*, ed. John Covington and Henry Nettleship (London, 1881). Cf. Ovid, *Fasti*, VI, 269–80, ed. and trans. James G. Frazer (London, 1929).

dwell. Consider how small a portion of it concerns you. For all the territory which you possess is narrow from north to south and, while broader from east to west, is in fact only a small island surrounded by the body of water which you on earth call either the Atlantic, or the Great Sea, or Oceanus.[17]

Eratosthenes had said that the inhabited world stretched over a third of the northern temperate zone which formed a complete circle, "itself meeting itself; so that, if the immensity of the Atlantic Sea did not prevent, we could sail from Iberia to India along one and the same parallel." [18] The Greek geographer Strabo affirmed Eratosthenes' statement, adding that "it may be that in this same temperate zone there are actually two inhabited worlds, or even more, and particularly in the proximity of the parallel through Athens that is drawn across the Atlantic Sea." [19] However, Strabo also said, "It is unlikely that the Atlantic Ocean is divided into two seas, thus being separated by isthmuses so narrow and that prevent circumnavigation; it is more likely that it is one confluent and continuous sea." [20] Strabo, who did not accept Eratosthenes' figures, had an overly optimistic idea of the small amount of yet unexplored ocean between India and Iberia. The "isthmuses" had to be narrow since, if they existed at all, they had to fit in the part that he considered unexplored.

Similarly optimistic speculation led to the dictum of Seneca: "How far is it from the utmost shores of Spain to those of India? But very few days' sail with a favoring wind." [21]

Aristotle taught that, although a frigid zone to the north and a torrid zone to the south limited the inhabited world, "the climate

[17] Cicero, *On the Commonwealth*, VI, 20, trans. George H. Sabine and Stanley B. Smith (Columbus, Ohio, 1929). This extended application of the term Atlantic stems from Herodotus and Eratosthenes, who applied it to all the ocean surrounding the "inhabited world." Cf. Diodorus Siculus, *Historical Library*, III, 38: ". . . the Red Sea and the Atlantic deep which stretches towards the South . . . "

[18] Quoted by Strabo, *Geography*, I, 4, vi.

[19] *Ibid.*

[20] *Ibid.*, I, 1, viii.

[21] Seneca, *Quaestiones Naturales*, Préface, 13, ed. Paul Oltramare (Paris, 1929): "Quantum est enim quod ab ultimis litoribus Hispaniae usque ad Indos jacet? Paucissimorum dierum spatium, si naven suus ferat uentus."

admits of its extending all round the earth. . . . There is nothing to prevent our travelling round the earth unless the extent of the sea presents an obstacle anywhere." [22] He also mentioned the possibility of a land to the south linking Africa and India. After citing the similarity of fauna, including elephants, he added, "Hence one should not be too sure of the incredibility of the view of those who conceive that there is continuity between the parts about the pillars of Hercules and the parts about India, and that in this way the ocean is one." [23]

The geographer Ptolemy thought that the southern part of Africa stretched eastward until it eventually joined with Asia, thus encircling the Indian Ocean. Belief in either a land-locked Atlantic or Indian Ocean would indicate that there were those who did not accept the accounts of African circumnavigation. Herodotus himself, in the case of Phoenician circumnavigation of that continent, was reporting what he had heard, not what he believed. In this instance his disbelief is likely. He did not feel that the ocean existed to the north of the inhabited world and thought that Europe stretched on indefinitely. He scoffed at contemporary cartographers, and said that he laughed "to see how many have ere now drawn maps of the world, not one of them showing the matter reasonably; for they draw the world as round as if fashioned by compasses, encircled by the river of Ocean, and Asia and Europe of a like bigness." [24] Herodotus was convinced of the veracity of another theory. He was of the continental rather than the oceanic school, believing that the land mass enclosed the seas.

In addition to the problem of the extent of the ocean and whether it enclosed the land or the land enclosed it, there were other problems which provoked thought and brought a variety of explanation from that first day when men went down to the sea.

How deep was it? Strangely enough most Mediterranean peoples thought that the Atlantic was shallower and calmer than their sea.

[22] Aristotle, *Meteorologica*, II, 5, trans. E. W. Webster (Oxford, 1923). In the same section he mentions the probability of a southern inhabited zone.

[23] Aristotle, *De Caelo*, II, 14.

[24] Herodotus, *History*, IV, 36.

It will serve our purpose to let Aristotle speak for antiquity. "Outside the pillars of Heracles," he said, "the sea is shallow owing to the mud, but calm, for it lies in a hollow." [25]

What formed the ocean currents and where, and from whence, did they flow? Most scholars of this period could not answer from experience, a fact which made theorizing even easier. According to Aristotle, the flow of the seas outside of the Mediterranean area was "not so easy to observe," but he offered an overall hypothesis that "just as single rivers flow from mountains, so it is with the earth as a whole: the greatest volume of water flows from the higher regions in the north." [26] Aristotle could not have been entirely satisfied with such an explanation, but it was the best he could do.

Whence the sea's salinity? Aristotle spent some time refuting theories advanced by others, often vehemently: "It is equally absurd to suppose that anything has been explained by calling the sea 'the sweat of the earth,' like Empedocles. Metaphors are poetical and so that expression of his may satisfy the requirements of a poem, but as a scientific theory it is unsatisfactory." [27] He finally decided that the saltiness of the ocean was caused by a substance "something like burnt earth," the undigested residue of nature which winds, especially those over hot dry regions, picked up. "Some quantity of this stuff must always be included in the clouds and the water that are formed by condensation, and must redescend to the earth in rain. This process must always go on with such regularity as the sublunary world admits of, and it is the answer to the question how the sea comes to be salt." [28] This was definitely not poetry, but it did have some scientific weaknesses. Aristotle had not—and rereading cannot alter the conclusion—answered the question at all.

What made the ocean ebb and flow? Since tides in the Mediterranean are barely apparent, Aristotle did not consider this as a problem. Pytheas and later Greeks and Romans, however, were aware of this phenomenon and of its relation to the phases of the moon. Posidonius of Rhodes (146–88 B.C.), another Greek geog-

[25] Aristotle, *Meteorologica*, II, 1.
[26] *Ibid.*
[27] *Ibid.*, II, 3.
[28] *Ibid.* See also Pliny, *Natural History*, II, 103.

rapher known to us through Strabo, may have been the first Mediterranean scientist to study Atlantic tidal phenomena on the spot, near Gades.[29] Pliny also related the tides to lunar influence, and gave an account of the diurnal, monthly, and annual tidal periods.[30] Caesar reported that his legions in Britain had the lunar influence on the sea impressed upon them by near disaster. Four days after peace was concluded with the Britons, a storm destroyed a number of his boats and made the others unseaworthy. Damage was especially great, Caesar explained, because it was "the night of the full moon." This was "the period of high tides at sea and the Romans did not know it." [31]

There was another question. Water was forever running into the sea. Why didn't it overflow? Aristotle's answer was evaporation.[32] Pliny thought otherwise. He ventured the opinion that the oceanic water made its way through veins in the earth and appeared once more, fresh, in wells and springs, ready to seek its way again to the sea.[33]

The classical idea of the earth as spherical is important to our

[29] The connection existing between the moon and the tides was, in many areas, a part of general knowledge, Cf. Mircea Eliade, *Patterns in Comparative Religion* (New York, 1963), 159:
> . . . All the moon divinities preserve more or less obvious water attributes or functions. To certain American Indian tribes, the moon, or the moon god, is at the same time the god of water. (This is true in Mexico, and among the Iroquois, to name two instances.) One tribe in central Brazil call the moon-god's daughter "Mother of the Waters." Hieronymo de Chaves said (in 1576), speaking of ancient Mexican beliefs concerning the moon, "the moon makes all things grow and multiply . . ." and "all moisture is governed by it." The link between the moon and the tides which both the Greeks and the Celts observed, was also known to the Maoris of New Zealand and the Eskimos (whose moon divinities govern the tides).

Aulus Gellius, in *Noctes Atticae*, XIV, 1 (New York, 1927), credits Chaldean astrologers with the observation that the sea was "the faithful companion of the moon." Re Posidonius, see Pierre Grimal, "Encyclopédies Antiques," *Journal of World History*, IX (1966), 463, 481. See also Strabo, *Geography*, III, 5, viii.

[30] Pliny, *Natural History*, II, 99.

[31] Julius Caesar, *Commentary on Gallic War*, IV, 29 (New York, 1917).

[32] Aristotle, *Meteorologica*, II, 2.

[33] Pliny, *Natural History*, II, 66. Cf. Homer, *Iliad*, XXI, 195–97, trans. A. T. Murray (New York, 1925): ". . . deep-flowing Ocean, from whom all rivers flow and every sea and all the springs and deep wells." See also Seneca, *Quaestiones Naturales*, III, 15 ff; Plato, *Phaedo*, 110–12.

study. This concept, which continued to be acceptable to some scholars during the Middle Ages, made possible scientific estimates of the size of the earth which were to play a major part in the era of conscious discovery. More specifically, it put definite limitations upon the expanse of ocean which lapped the shores of Europe on the west. Such a view impressed upon some how little of the world was known, and at the same time made apparent to others the possibility of knowing all of the earth, at least within the northern temperate zone.

The view that the equator formed an impassable barrier was not shared by all, although this theory was upheld by Aristotle. Experience both in the Atlantic and the Indian Ocean opposed it. The Sahara served to assure the half-wise and the weak-hearted that it was so. Unfortunately the Romans tended to leave the commercial ventures which involved extensive travel over land and sea to the least Roman and, frequently (for business reasons), less vocal members of their world. Now we must also share their silence.

III *Somewhere They Had Never Traveled*

THE MOST famous of the Atlantic islands never existed as a land mass, and has never died as an idea. The story of Atlantis was injected into our traditional culture by Plato in the middle of the fourth century before Christ. It appeared in two of his Socratic dialogues, the *Timaeus* and the *Critias*. In the *Timaeus*, the Athenian Critias purports to retell an account which the great lawgiver Solon had heard in Egypt:

Many great and wonderful deeds are recorded of your state in our [Egyptian] histories. But one of them exceeds all the rest in greatness and valour. For these histories tell of a mighty power which unprovoked made an expedition against the whole of Europe and Asia, and to which your city put an end. This power came forth out of the Atlantic Ocean, *for in those days the Atlantic was navigable;* and there was an island situated in front of the straits which are by you called the Pillars of Heracles; the island was larger than Libya and Asia put together, and was the way to other islands, *and from these you might pass . . .* [to] *the opposite continent which surrounded the true ocean;* for this sea which is within the Straits of Heracles is only a harbour, having a narrow entrance, but that other is a real sea, and the surrounding land may most truly be called *a boundless continent.* Now in this island of Atlantis there was a great and wonderful empire which had rule over the whole island and several others, and *over parts of the continent,* and, furthermore, the men of Atlantis had subjected the parts of Libya within the columns of Heracles as far as Egypt, and of Europe as far as Tyrrhenia. This vast power, gathered into one, endeavoured to subdue at a blow our country and yours and the whole of the region within the straits; and then, Solon, your country shone forth, in the excellence of her virtue and strength, among all mankind. She was pre-eminent in courage and military skill, and was the leader of the Hellenes. And when the rest fell off from her, being compelled to stand alone, after having undergone the very extremity of danger, she defeated and triumphed over the invaders, and preserved from slavery those who were not yet subjugated, and generously liberated all the rest of us who dwell within the pillars. But afterwards there occurred violent earthquakes and floods; and in a single day and night of misfortune all your warlike men in a body sank into the earth, and the island of Atlantis in like manner disappeared in the depths of the sea. For which reason *the sea in those parts is impassable and impenetrable, because there is such a shoal of mud in the way;* and this was caused by the subsidence of the island.[1]

[1] Plato, *Timaeus,* 24–25. The italics are this author's. Because of the importance of the meaning attached to various phrases in this passage, a variant translation follows, from Francis Macdonald Cornford, *Plato's Cosmology: The Timaeus of Plato Translated with a Running Commentary* (New York, 1957):

Many great exploits of your city are here recorded for the admiration of all; but one surpasses the rest in greatness and valour. The records tell how great a power your city once brought to an end when it insolently advanced against all Europe and Asia, starting from the Atlantic ocean outside. For in those days that ocean could be crossed, since there was an island in it in front of the strait which your countrymen tell me you call the Pillars of Heracles. The Island was larger than Libya and Asia put together; and from it the voyagers of those days could reach the other islands, and from these islands the whole of the opposite continent bounding that ocean which truly deserves the name. For all these parts that lie within the strait I speak of, seem to be a bay with a narrow entrance; that outer sea is the real ocean, and the land which entirely surrounds it really deserves the name of continent in the proper sense. Now on this Atlantic island there had grown up an extraordinary power under kings who ruled not only the whole island but many of the other islands and parts of the continent; and besides that, within the straits, they were lords of Libya so far as to Egypt, and of Europe to the borders of Tyrrhenia. All this power, gathered into one, attempted at one swoop to enslave your country and ours and all the region within the strait. Then it was, Solon, that the power of your city was made manifest to all mankind in its valour and strength. She was foremost of all in courage and in the arts of war, and first as the leader of Hellas, then forced by the defection of the rest to stand alone, she faced the last extreme of danger, vanquished the invaders, and set up her trophy; the peoples not yet enslaved she preserved from slavery, and all the rest of us who dwell within the bounds set by Heracles she freed with ungrudging hand. Afterwards there was a time of inordinate earthquakes and floods; there came one terrible day and night, in which all your men of war were swallowed bodily by the earth, and the island Atlantis also sank beneath the sea and vanished. Hence to this day that outer ocean cannot be crossed or explored, the way being blocked by mud, just below the surface, left by the settling down of the island.

In a footnote to this passage, Cornford comments: "Serious scholars now

Plato returned to the Atlantis theme in the *Critias,* an imaginative expansion of the foregoing which apparently never was finished.

The hypothesis that the legend of Atlantis' destruction had as prototype a volcanic eruption on the Aegean island of Santorin and an accompanying flood has recently received much attention in the news media. This theory states that a misunderstanding as to date and to the size of the land mass involved led Plato to transfer the catastrophic locale to the Atlantic. Professor Angelo Galanopoulos' investigations in the Aegean have led him to maintain such a position. Galanopoulos has removed what he felt was an intrusive zero, which reduces the 9,000-year span separating the catastrophe and Solon's account thereof to 900 years. He justified the dropping of the zero because "it corrected an error of space as well as an error of time in Plato's account of Atlantis. When adjusted downward to fit the new scale of measurement, the immense size of the plain Plato included in Atlantis came easily within the limits of the Aegean Sea." Galanopoulos reasoned that "the same sort of error must be compensated for today whenever an Englishman and an American talk in terms of billions. . . . The ancient Greeks had similar troubles in reading the glyphs of Egypt." [2] Whatever the prototype, the Atlantic became the locale or at least the last mythographic resting place of Atlantis.

Even if Plato were resorting to myth to reinforce a philosophical point, the tale of Atlantis, nevertheless, reveals something of the educated fourth century (B.C.) Greek view of the Atlantic. It separated the known world from another continent. It could no longer be crossed because of mud shoals. The transatlantic continent, although inaccessible, was certainly inhabitable, since part of the Atlantis empire supposedly had been established there.

Considerable Greek interest in this other continent existed.

---

agree that Atlantis probably owed its existence entirely to Plato's imagination." See also Rachel L. Carson, *The Sea Around Us* (New York, 1951), 72–73.

[2] John Lear, "The Volcano That Shaped the Western World," *Saturday Review,* XLIX (November, 1966), 66. See also Angelos C. Galanopoulos, "Letters to the Science Editor," *Saturday Review,* XLIX (December, 1966), 93, and XLX (April, 1967), 56; "Atlantis and the Searchers," *Newsweek,* LXX (July, 1967), 52–55.

Aelian (c. A.D. 125), for example, cited the no longer extant writings of Theopompus, a contemporary of Plato, as source for the statement that "Silenus, the satyr, had told Midas that Europe, Asia and Africa were islands surrounded by the ocean and that there was but one continent, which was beyond this world and large beyond belief.³ The people who inhabited the outer continent lived twice as long and were twice the size of ordinary men, Theopompus wrote. One warlike nation among them once planned a voyage to the insular regions of Europe, Asia, and Africa. Ten million of them sailed across the ocean. However, after looking around, they decided that the territory was not worth conquering and went home.⁴

Strabo, some three centuries later, quoted a passage from Posidonius, a friend and tutor of Cicero, which stated that the Atlantis tale might not be fiction. Posidonius had taken exception to an earlier critic who held that "its inventor caused it [Atlantis] to disappear, just as did the Poet [Homer] the wall of the Achaeans." ⁵ Pliny the Elder was more cautious. Atlantis was a case of a land being swept completely away by the sea "if we accept Plato's story." Elsewhere, however, he acknowledged an island by that name to exist in the Atlantic.⁶ Plutarch thought that the account of Atlantis could be either history or fable, although he was sure that the story came from Egypt via Solon.⁷

Then slowly all doubt began to fade. In Alexandria, the Jewish philosopher Philo accepted the account as true:

And the island of Atlantis "greater than Libya and Asia put together," as Plato says in the *Timaeus*, "in a single day and night through extraordinary earthquakes and floods sank below the sea and suddenly disappeared," turning into a sea that was not navigable but full of abysses. So then the fiction which they propound that the sea is di-

---

³ Aelian, *Varia Historia*, III, 18 (London, 1701).
⁴ *Ibid.*
⁵ Strabo, *Geography*, II, 3, vi. Cf. Strabo XIII, 1, xxxvi. ". . . for Homer says that the wall had only recently been built (Or else it was not built at all, but fabricated and then abolished by the poet, as Aristotle says). . . ."
⁶ Pliny, *Natural History*, II, 92; VI, 36.
⁷ Plutarch, *Solon*, 31.

minished contributes nothing to show that the world is destroyed for it is clear that the sea withdraws from some places and inundates others.[8]

Aelian, writing in the first half of the second century A.D., in addition to the reference to a transoceanic continent already cited, referred directly to Atlantis. He informed his readers that the ancient kings and queens of Atlantis bound their heads with the skins of sea rams, citing "the people who live by the ocean" as his source.[9] Aelian accepted the historicity of Atlantis and, moreover, buttressed it by the testimony of coastal inhabitants.

The Roman historian Ammianus Marcellinus in the fourth century A.D. also accepted the Atlantis of Plato as factual. He told of earthquakes (*chasmatiae*) suddenly rending the earth and swallowing huge portions of it, and cited Atlantis as an example.[10]

A century later, the Neoplatonist Proclus, in his commentary on the *Timaeus*, said that an early "interpreter" of Plato named Krantor had vouched for the truth of the Platonic account by testifying that the Egyptians still preserved pillars with the story of Atlantis inscribed upon them. Proclus also noted that a first-century B.C. geographer, Marcellus, reported that on certain remote Atlantic islands the people preserved traditions of Atlantis. Proclus' conclusion was that "*it is not proper to disbelieve what is said by Plato.*" [11]

A Latin translation and commentary on the *Timaeus* was made in the third century by Chalcidius, and the West had an opportunity to familiarize itself with Plato's Atlantis. In fact until the

[8] Philo, *On the Eternity of the World*, XXVI, trans. F. H. Colson (Cambridge, Mass., 1941).

[9] Aelian, *De Natura Animalium* (London, 1744), XV, 2: "Ceterum oceani accolae fabulantur veteres Atlantidis reges, qui genus ad Neptunum referunt, in capitibus suis arietum marium taenias gestasse, imperii insigne; et reginas similiter cirros feminarum arietum."

[10] Ammianus Marcellinus, *History*, XVII, 7, xiii, trans. John C. Rolfe (Cambridge, Mass., 1935): ". . . as in the Atlantic Ocean an island more extensive than all Europe, and in the Crisaean Gulf, Helice and Bura; and in the Ciminian district of Italy the town of Saccumum; these were all sunk into the deep abysses of Erebus, and lie hidden in eternal darkness. . . ."

[11] Proclus, *Commentaries on Plato's Timaeus*, I, included in Appendix to L. Sprague deCamp, *Lost Continents* (New York, 1954), 309–10. The italics are this author's. See also Geoffrey Ashe, *Land to the West*, 190–92.

twelfth century this was the only work by Plato available to scholars in Latin.[12]

In the *Periplus of Scylax*, written in the fourth century B.C., reefs and mud banks were reported to extend across the Atlantic from the outermost point of Africa to that of Europe, thus restricting navigation. This misinformation might have been based upon the Platonic account; on the other hand, Carthaginian propaganda or Aristotelian science might have been equally responsible. The passage in Scylax's *Periplus* reads:

> After the Pillars of Heracles, as you sail into the outer spaces, having Libya on your left, there is a great gulf extending as far as Cape Hermaeum. . . . From Point Hermaeum onwards stretch great reefs, in fact from Libya towards Europe, not rising above the surface of the sea, though in some places breakers flood in on them. This barrier of rocks stretches to another headland opposite in Europe, the name of this headland being the Sacred Promontory. . . . The stretches of sea beyond Cerne are not further navigable because of the shallows of the sea and because of the mud and seaweed; the seaweed is one hand's breadth in width and at the tip is sharp enough to prick.[13]

These accounts of an unfriendly and unnavigable ocean whose very mud banks were silent reminders of an earlier disaster were balanced by others. One pseudo-Aristotelian tale concerned an Atlantic island discovered by the Carthaginians.[14] This report may have vaguely reflected an actual discovery. The island was fortunate in its resources, and it was admirable for its fruits—a quality shared by many real and imaginary Atlantic islands. The Hesper-

[12] Cf. deCamp, *Lost Continents*, 19; Fernand van Steenberghen, *Aristotle in the West* (Louvain, 1955), 64.

[13] Scylax, *Periplus*, 112, trans. E. P. Warmington, in *Greek Geography* (New York, 1934), 140–41.

[14] Aristotle (pseudo), *De Mirabilibus Auscultationibus*, 84:
> In the sea outside the Pillars of Hercules they say that an island was discovered by the Carthaginians, desolate, having wood of every kind, and navigable rivers, and admirable for its fruits besides, but distant several days' voyage from them. But when the Carthaginians often came to this island because of its fertility, and some even dwelt there, the magistrates of the Carthaginians gave notice that they would punish with death those who should sail to it, and destroyed all the inhabitants lest they should spread a report about it, or a large number might gather together to the island in their time, get possession of the authority, and destroy the prosperity of the Carthaginians.

ides produced their golden apples. Avalon, "the isle of apples," was featured in Celtic myth. Vinland *The Good* of the Vikings would abound in grapes.

The same pseudo-Aristotelian work offered another interesting bit of information on the Atlantic:

They say that the Phoenicians who inhabit the city called Gades, when they sail outside the Pillars of Heracles under an easterly wind for four days, arrive at certain desolate places, full of rushes and sea weed, and that these places are not covered with water, whenever there is an ebb, but, whenever there is a flood, they are overflowed, and in these there is found an exceeding great number of tunnies, of a size and thickness surpassing belief, when they are stranded. These they salt, pack up in vessels, and convey to Carthage. They are the only fish which the Carthaginians do not export; on account of their excellence for food, they consume them themselves.[15]

Here a factual report of that with which the Carthaginians returned to port was combined with a fantastic version of how or where it was obtained. The rushes and seaweed were reminiscent of Himilco's voyages; the reefs, of those in the *Periplus* of Scylax.

Atlantic monsters were reported frequently in classical times and grew more monstrous with the passing centuries. In the pages of Strabo's *Geography* were found some rather moderate terrors:

For the various kinds of oysters as well as mussels are in general surpassing, both in their number and in their size, along the whole of the exterior sea. . . . So it is, in the same way, with respect to . . . spouting-whales; when these spout, the distant observer seems to see a cloud-like pillar. And further the conger-eels become monsters, far exceeding in size those of Our Sea; and so do the lampreys and several other edible fish of the kind.[16]

"Large numbers of plump, fat, tunny-fish" were described as feeding on the fruit of the "sea oak" which grew in great abundance on the sea floor far out in the Atlantic.

Another pseudo-Aristotelian account, the *De Mundo*, which probably dates from the second century after Christ, theorized

---

[15] *Ibid.*, 136.
[16] Strabo, *Geography*, III, 2, vii. Cf. DeLatil and Rivoire, *Man and the Underwater World*, 60–121.

transoceanic land masses "separated from ours by a sea that we must cross to reach them, some larger and others smaller than it, but all, save our own invisible to us." [17]

Although Pytheas in the fourth century B.C. had offered his readers a great deal of knowledge concerning the North Atlantic and the countries upon which it bordered, most of this failed to be accepted by the Mediterranean world. The geographer Strabo gave Pytheas rather unpleasant billing; the latter's name, which appeared with some frequency in Strabo's *Geography*, was always burdened with invective. Strabo argued that Ireland, and not Thule as Pytheas had said, was the most northerly of inhabitable countries: "For not only has the man who tells about Thule, Pytheas, been found, upon scrutiny, to be an arch-falsifier, but the men who have seen Britain and Ierne [Ireland] do not mention Thule, though they speak of other islands, small ones, about Britain." [18]

Pliny the Elder mentioned the island of Britain or "Albion," and all the islands clustered around it. He said that the British Isles or "The Britains" included Hibernia, the Orkneys, the Shetlands, the Hebrides, the islands between Albion and Hibernia, and so forth. More remote was Thule, in which there were "no nights at midsummer when the sun is passing through the sign of the Crab and on the other hand no days at midwinter." [19] Pliny had mentioned this last fact earlier in discussing how daylight varied with latitude, and at this time cited Pytheas with no apparent approbation or distrust. He simply said that "Pytheas of Marseilles writes that this occurs in the Island of Thule, 6 days' voyage N. from Britain." [20]

At this point Pliny, citing a work no longer extant, reported that the historian Timaeus told of an island called Mictis "lying inward [within?] six days' sail from Britain where tin is found, and to which the Britains cross in boats of osier covered with stitched

[17] Aristotle (pseudo), *De Mundo*, III, trans. E. S. Forster (Oxford, 1914).

[18] Strabo, *Geography*, I, 4, iii.

[19] Pliny, *Natural History*, IV, 16.

[20] *Ibid.*, II, 77. Here he says they have six months of day followed by six months of night in that region.

hides." [21] He also mentioned islands discussed by other writers, including the Scandiae, Dumna, Bergos, and one, "the largest of all from which the crossing to Thule starts" which was named Berrice or Nerigos. The latter reference might be to the island of Lewis which lies northwest of Scotland.[22]

One day's sail from Thule, Pliny located the frozen sea, the "mare concretum," called the Cronian Sea or Cronium Ocean.[23] The name of the god Cronus, father of Zeus, was associated by Pindar and other Greeks with the Islands of the Blest in the Atlantic.[24] Plutarch, biographer and essayist, provided material which helps us connect Pindar's "tower of Cronus" on the western Islands of the Blest with the Cronian Sea in the frozen north. His essay *On the Face which appears on the Orb of the Moon* contained the following: " 'Far o'er the brine an isle Ogygian lies,' distant from Britain five day's sail to the West. There are three other islands equidistant from Britain and from one another in the general direction of the sun's summer setting. The natives have a story that in one of these Cronus has been confined by Zeus." [25] Elsewhere, in his essay *On the Cessation of Oracles*, Plutarch supplied information supplemental to this. The time was A.D. 83–84, and Demetrius of Tarsus had recently returned from Britain.

Demetrius told us that, among the islands near Britain, many were

[21] *Ibid.*, IV, 16: ". . . a Britannia introrsum sex dierum navigatione abesse . . ."

[22] The Loeb edition of Pliny's *Natural History*, IV, 16 has "Berricen, ex qua in Tylen navigetur." Others have "Nerigon, ex qua in Thulen navigetur", e.g., G. Brotier (ed.), Pliny, *Natural History* (London, 1826). The Bostock and Riley translation of Pliny's *Natural History* (London, 1887) uses the latter text and in a note suggests (I, 352) that Nerigos is equatable with the island of Lewis, "the northern promotory of which is in the old maps designated by the name of Nary or Nery." See also Nansen, *In Northern Mists*, I, 107.

[23] Pliny, *Natural History*, IV, 13; IV, 16.

[24] Cf. Pindar, *Olympian Odes*, II, 68–76; Hesiod, *Theogony*, 729–48.

[25] Plutarch, *On the Face which Appears on the Orb of the Moon*, 26 trans. A. O. Prickard, in *Selected Essays of Plutarch* (Oxford, 1918), II. For the source of Plutarch's quotation, see Homer, *Odyssey*, VII: "There is an isle, Ogygia, that lies far off the coast in the sea; therein dwells the fair-tressed daughter of Atlas, guileful Calypso. . . ." Concerning the island of Cronus see Ashe, *Land to the West*, 215–16.

deserted and lay scattered (Sporades), some of them bearing the names of demons and demigods.[26] He himself, by the Emperor's command, made a voyage of inquiry and observation to the nearest of the deserted islands, which had a few inhabitants, *all sacred persons* and never molested by the Britons. . . . They [the islanders] added that there is one island in particular where Cronus is a prisoner, being guarded in his sleep by Briareus; for sleep has been devised to be a chain to bind him, and there are many daemons about him as satellites and attendants.[27]

This voyage of inquiry to a holy island in the sea beyond Britain cannot help but remind us of the voyage of Germanicus. Demetrius, however, was apparently successful. If we return to the first dialogue, *On the Face which appears on the Orb of the Moon*, other echoes are heard. The "other side," and "the outermost shores of the world" are here: "To the great continent by which the ocean is fringed is a voyage of about five thousand stades [c. 612 miles], made in row-boats from Ogygia, of less from the other islands." [28] Not only that, but the sea is described as difficult to sail through. Demetrius explained that the sea was slow of passage and full of mud "because of the number of streams which the great mainland discharges, forming alluvial tracts and making the sea heavy like land." [29]

"One day's sail from Thule," Pliny had said, was "the frozen ocean called by some the Cronian Sea." Plutarch reported the sea near Cronus' oceanic prison as being "heavy like land whence an opinion prevailed that it was actually frozen." [30]

The remainder of the account was equally fanciful and owed a great deal to the imagination. Much of the imaginary, however, seems to have been composed in quilt-like fashion of patches of tradition and hearsay rather than out of whole cloth. There were supposedly Greeks living on the outer continent, some of whom "came with Hercules and were left behind by him." (One won-

[26] Pillars of Heracles?

[27] Plutarch, *On the Cessation of Oracles*, 18, in *Selected Essays*, trans. A. O. Prickard and T. G. Tucker (Oxford, 1913–18). For some intriguing speculation concerning this passage, see Ashe, *Land to the West*, 215–16, 311.

[28] Plutarch, *On the Face which Appears on the Orb of the Moon*, 26.

[29] *Ibid.*

[30] *Ibid.*

ders if rumor reported Pillars of Heracles there.) On some of the outlying islands, the inhabitants "day after day, for thirty days, see the sun hidden for less than one hour." [31] Moreover all this was attributed to Sextius Sylla, a Carthaginian whom Plutarch referred to elsewhere as a man wanting neither learning nor ingenuity.[32]

Sylla also reported that every thirty years, which was one year of the star of Cronus (the planet Saturn), the Carthaginians outfitted an expedition to these North Atlantic islands where Cronus was a prisoner of sleep. The members of these expeditions relieved others who had sailed there thirty years before to serve the god. Many of these, however, preferred not to leave, "some because they have grown used to it, some because all things are there in plenty without pain or trouble, while their life is passed in sacrifices and festivals or given to literature or philosophy. For the natural beauty of the isle is wonderful, the mildness of the environing air." [33] Sylla, who we must admit combined learning with ingenuity, claimed to have heard all this from one who had put in his thirty years and returned.

Another suggested derivation of Cronium as a name for this sea is from the Germanic adjective *groen* or green.[34] Others have noted that in the Irish tongue *muir croinn* denotes "a thick, co-agulated, frozen sea." [35] The latter suggestion is attractive, but it has not been established that the term was ever used with this meaning. The Celtic *cruinn*, which I assume must be the adjective meant, is translated as "full, round, circular, globular, assembled, gathered up, compact" and, I suppose by extension, "thick." The word *cron* may mean a "hindrance," which would help the case; but *cron* may also mean, "copper," "time," or "Cronus," which does not help much.

In support of the "green" faction (Shades of Byzantium!), one might offer two bits of circumstantial evidence. The Irish did have a special name for a dark green sea; this was *crontsaile*. More striking is the twelfth-century testimony of Adam of Bremen. In dis-

[31] *Ibid.*
[32] Plutarch, *Life of Romulus*, 15.
[33] Plutarch, *On the Face which Appears on the Orb of the Moon*, 26.
[34] Bostock and Riley (eds.), *Pliny's Natural History*, I, 342 n.
[35] *Classical Journal*, II (1812), 297.

cussing Greenland, he said the country received its name from the Cerulean Sea.[36] The fact that he also seemed to attribute this color to its inhabitants is a problem which happily does not concern us here.

As Plutarch has pointed out, "geographers thrust into the extremities of their maps those countries that are unknown to them, remarking, at the same time, that all beyond is hills of sand and haunts of wild beast, frozen seas, marshes, and mountains that are inaccessible to human courage or industry." [37] Frequently, marvelous things heard concerning somewhere they had never traveled misled them. Occasionally, with the help of good fortune or a good informant, they were right.

[36] Adam of Bremen, *Gesta Hammaburgensis Ecclesiae Pontificum*, IV, 36, ed. J. P. Migne, (Paris, 1882), CXLVI: "Homines ibi a salo cerulei; unde et regio illa nomen accepit." For another tangential connection of Cronus (Latin=Saturn) with the Atlantic, cf. *Schol. ad Dionys. Perieg.* in Müller's *Fragmenta Historicorum Graecorum*, III, 640: "Hae primum Saturni columnae nominabantur, quod hucusque regnum ejus pertineret; deinde dicebantur Briarei columnae, ut Euphorio ait, tum vero Herculis."
[37] Plutarch, *Theseus*, 1, in *Plutarch's Lives*, trans. John and William Langhorne (New York, 1889).

IV *Scholars at Sea*

THE *Chorographia* of Pomponius Mela, written in Spain in the middle of the first century, leaves much scholarship to be desired. As a geographical treatise, however, the work by its very unscholarly nature gives us a glimpse of the world and oceanic view of the average citizen at that time.[1] According to Mela, the world was included in a circle (*uno ambitu*) and the earth, surrounded by water, was divided by an equatorial ocean. Below this ocean there was another inhabited land mass. To the west of Europe was the Atlantic; to the north, the Britannic ocean. Mela buttressed his argument that the ocean to the north of Europe was not only continuous but sailable by citing from Cornelius Nepos an account of Indians who had been driven by storm to the German coast. He was rather undecided about the cause of tides. The moon might be responsible; submarine caverns could be involved; or the tides might be caused by the earth's breathing.[2]

The Cassiterides, or Tin Islands, were placed by Mela in the western ocean. These were distinct from Britain and from Ireland (Juverna), which was above or beyond (*super*) Britain. He also mentioned the Orcades (Orkneys) and the Haemodae (Shetlands?) as island groups. Thule, he said, was opposite the shores of the Belcae[3] who lived far to the north in that part of Europe bordering on Asia.[4] In Thule, Mela continued, the nights were light throughout the summer, and during the solstice there was no

[1] Burton, *Discovery of the Ancient World*, 77.
[2] Mela, *De Chorographia*, I, 1; I, 3; III, 1; III, 5.
[3] *Ibid.*, III, 6: "Thyle Belcarum litori adposita est, Grais et nostris celebrata carminibus."
[4] *Ibid.*, III, 5: "Inde Asiae confinia nisi ubi perpetuae hiemes sedent et intolerabilis rigor. Scythici populi incolunt, fere omnes et in unum Belcae adpellati."

night at all because the greater part of the sun remained above the horizon.[5]

Mela touched on the African voyage of Hanno, and the reported circumnavigation of that continent by Eudoxus. He also mentioned the Gorgades, off the African coast, where some said the Gorgons lived. The islands of the Hesperides were off the African coast farther to the north. Still farther north, opposite Mt. Atlas, were the Fortunate Islands, fertile in soil and abundant in crops which continually reseeded themselves. Those who lived there were wanting in nothing. Here also, according to Mela, were two amazing fountains. Those who drank would laugh themselves to death. This was somewhat *unfortunate*, but things were not as bad as they might have been; a drink from the other cured anything, including, one trusts, a deathly fit of laughter.[6]

About A.D. 120 a certain Dionysius Periegetes wrote a poem in Greek based upon old Greek sources which purported to be a description of the inhabited world.[7] In this poem, many traditional concepts were presented which were at variance with the scientific knowledge of the day. The world of Dionysius was a flat oblong land mass surrounded by ocean and floating on mythological illusions. The *Periegesis* of Dionysius was translated and made available to the Latin-speaking West by Avienus in the fourth century and Priscian in the sixth century.[8] The fact that the volume was out-of-date when first issued was not considered to detract from its value. Then as now this was standard for text books. It has been summed up as a "curious piece of doggerel . . . hardly significant except as the sort of rehash of older matter served up in school teaching." [9]

One of the greatest names in ancient geography was that of Claudius Ptolemy who lived in Alexandria about A.D. 150. He made

[5] *Ibid.,* III, 6. There is some confusion in the passage. Mela adds that the nights in winter are short and dark.

[6] *Ibid.,* III, 9–10: "Una singulari duorum fontium ingenio maxime insignis; alterum qui gustavere risu solvuntur in mortem; ita adfectis remedium est ex altero bibere."

[7] Dionysius Periegetes, *Periegesis,* ed. G. Bernhardy (Leipzig, 1828).

[8] *Ibid.* Both these Latin translations are included in the above volume, plus Bernhardy's own Latin translation of the Greek text.

[9] Thomson, *History of Ancient Geography,* 235.

an attempt to map the whole of the known world. His text, cryptic and uninteresting, was composed primarily of lists of places followed by each one's latitude and longitude.

Ptolemy's information regarding Britain, Ireland, and the surrounding islands was more exact than that of his predecessors. He located Thule to the northeast of Britain and he may have considered it to be what is today Norway.[10]

In the Atlantic, off the northwest tip of Spain, he placed two groups of islands, the Cassiterides and the Islands of the Gods. Further south, off the African coast were Cerne, Autolala, and the Islands of the Blest.[11]

Ptolemy, however, made almost no immediate impression on the Latin West. His *System of Astronomy* (*Almagest*) was highly regarded by the Moslem world and through them was introduced into western Europe in the twelfth century. His *Geography* would not be translated into Latin until A.D. 1410.

Ptolemy's was actually the last forward step in ancient geography, but he walked alone and had few followers. The rest was retrogression. Soon Strabo's *Geography* also lost what popularity it had. The *Natural History* of the elder Pliny, which was more attuned to the temper of the times, held its own. Many admirers busily mined its pages.

Solinus was a third-century pagan compiler of a book of marvels, the *Collectanea Rerum Memorabilium*. He used geography primarily as a pegboard upon which to hang his wonders. His conviction that fact could never hold a candle to fancy gained him the extravagant respect of the Middle Ages.[12] Those sections of Solinus' book of marvels which touched upon the Atlantic were based largely upon Pliny's *Natural History*.

Solinus for the most part repeated Pliny's account of Britain, Ireland, and Thule,[13] but had information from another source concerning an island called Tanatus. This was obviously the little

[10] Ptolemy, *Geography*, II, 1–2, trans. E. L. Stevenson (New York, 1932).
[11] *Ibid.*, 5–6.
[12] Thomson, *History of Ancient Geography*, 373.
[13] Solinus, *Collectanea Rerum Memorabilium*, ed. Theodor Mommsen (Berlin, 1895), XXII, 1, 2, 9, 10. His view of tides is comparable to Mela's.

island of Thanet off the northeast coast of Kent,[14] but in Solinus' pages it assumed unusual importance. It was a fortunate (*felix*) island with fields of grain and fruitful soil. Tanatus was, moreover, free from snakes.[15] Solinus indeed launched the fact of Thanet on a fanciful career.

Following Pliny, Solinus placed the Cassiterides, rich in tin, off the Iberian Peninsula. Near these were the Fortunate Islands, at least one of which was snakeless.[16] Off the African coast were the Gorgades, above these the Hesperides, and off Mauretania another group of Fortunate Islands.[17]

A surprisingly large amount of oceanic material was provided by the "last poet of Classical Rome," Claudius Claudianus, who lived at the end of the fourth century. His Atlantic was still, at least poetically, intimately connected with the spirits which had "gone west." Although he did not mention the island of Tanatus, whose importance was stressed by Solinus (and whose name resembled the Greek word for death, *Thanatos*), Claudian reported:

> There is a place where Gaul stretches her furthermost shore spread out before the waves of Ocean: 'tis there that Ulysses is said to have called up the silent ghosts with a libation of blood. There is heard the mournful weeping of the spirits of the dead as they flit by with faint

[14] Eilert Ekwall, *Concise Oxford Dictionary of English Place-names* (Oxford, 1936), 443: "THANET [in] K[ent] (Tanatus 3[rd. Century] Solinus, *Tanatos* c 730 Bede. . . .) The name is identical or cognate with the river-name TANAT. It may mean 'bright island' or 'fire island' (from a beacon or light house)."

[15] Solinus, *Collectanea*, XXII, 8: "at Tanatus insula adspiratur freto Gallico, a Brittaniae continente aestuario tenui separata, felix frumentariis campis et gleba uberi, nec tantum sibi verum et aliis salubris locis: nam cum ipsa nullo serpatur angue, asportata inde terra quoquo gentium invecta sit angues necat."

[16] *Ibid.*, XXIII, 10: "Cassiterides insulae spectant adversum Celtiberiae latus, plumbi fertiles: et tres Fortunatae, e quibus solum vocabulum signandum fuit. Ebusus . . . serpentum non habet: utpote cuius terra serpentes fuget." Cf. Pliny, *Natural History*, IV, 22: "Ex adverso Celtiberiae conplures sunt insulae Cassiterides dictae Graecis a fertilitate plumbi albi, et e regione Arrotrebarum promunturi Deorum VI, quas aliqui Fortunatas appellavere."

[17] *Ibid.*, LVI, 10–19.

sound of wings, and the inhabitants see the pale ghosts pass and the shades of the dead.[18]

Claudian also dealt with Thule, but his testimony was not entirely consistent. He assured the general Stilicho that his men would follow him "even as far as Thule lying icebound beneath the pole-star."[19] This may have been rather cold comfort since he referred elsewhere to Thule as a place "whither no ship can sail."[20] On the other hand, Thule was more inaccessible in 396 than in the year 400. On the latter date Claudian proclaimed: "To her [Rome's] rule of peace we owe it that the world is our home, that we can live where we please, and that to visit Thule and explore its once dreaded wilds is but a sport."[21]

Claudian's conception of Thule seemed to have changed in the interim. He had followed his earlier reference to "Thule whither no ship can sail" by relating how Theodosius, the grandfather of Honorius, fought in Africa and in Britain. He declared further that Theodosius' "adventurous oars broke the surface of the northern seas."[22] This General Theodosius was the father of the emperor Theodosius I. Since Theodosius I firmly entrenched Christianity as the state religion of Rome, he might have merited being called "holy" by Dicuil. The likelihood that the emperor would have been interested in exploration is great. Consider Claudian's account of the activities of the emperor's father:

Theodosius . . . brought into subjection the coasts of Britain and . . . laid waste the north. . . . What avail against him the eternal snows, the frozen air, the uncharted sea? The Orcades ran red with Saxon slaughter; Thule was warm with the blood of Picts; ice-bound Hibernia wept for the heaps of slain Scots. [And in the south, Theodosius] . . . beheld the Gorgon's empoisoned lair, and laughed to see the common verdure of those gardens of the Hesperides which story had clothed with gold.[23]

---

[18] Claudian, *Against Rufinus*, I, 123–28, in *Works*, trans. Maurice Platnauer (New York, 1922).

[19] *Ibid.*, II, 239–40.

[20] Claudian, *Third Consulship of Honorius*, 53.

[21] Claudian, *On Stilicho's Consulship*, III, 154–57.

[22] Claudian, *Third Consulship of Honorius*, 54–56: ". . . fregit Hyperboreas remis audacibus undas."

[23] Claudian, *Fourth Consulship of Honorius*, 24–38. On the mobility of Thule, see Cassidy, "The Voyage of an Island," 595–602.

A Pictish Thule and an ice-bound Hibernia are hardly convincing, but, on the other hand, the "common verdure" of the Hesperides has a truthful ring.

Most of the later classical scholars were firmly convinced that the land mass which made up the "inhabited world" was completely surrounded by water; though there were others who held that the ocean, or oceans, was surrounded by land. Some exponents of this latter "continental" hypothesis, such as Herodotus and Ptolemy, were not available to the West until late in the Middle Ages. References to the "outer continent" and the "other side" were much too common to disappear completely. In the Scandinavian north, for example, there would evolve the theory that the outer continent made a mediterranean sea of the Atlantic and was in turn surrounded by an outer ocean. Therefore, although an "oceanic" view was the one most prominently presented and most readily accepted by the early Christian scholars, this view was capable of a great deal of variation both in antiquity and in the Middle Ages. There might be one "inhabited world" surrounded by an ocean which had no outer limits but infinity; there could be a great continent surrounding the ocean, which might or might not be crossed.

Crates of Mallus, in the second century before Christ, had propounded a theory of four equal land masses separated by an ocean girdling the globe at the equator and again from pole to pole. The spectre of an antipodal human population not related to Noah and not descended from Adam, however, made Christians who held this view suspect.[24] It was unthinkable that intelligent forms of life might exist in such inaccessible regions.

During the Middle Ages the idea of a spherical earth lost ground but it did not disappear. A great many classical geographical concepts remained, and the ocean was still there for personal obser-

[24] Nothing is more illustrative of the way problems keep reappearing in new guises than the comparison between the problem posed by theorized existence of humans on the other side of an "impassable" equator who, if they did exist, could not be descendants of Adam and the problem posed to the Christian church today by the theoretical existence of life on planets other than our own. Cf. Norman W. Pittenger, "Christianity and the Man on Mars," *Christian Century*, LXXIII (1956), 747–48.

vation. A new factor had been added to scholarship, however. The Christian had a source which he felt to be less fallible than his senses, more trustworthy than the testimony of antiquity. In the Bible he had the very word of God.

Geographical data was not abundant in the Bible but fervent Christian scholars searched diligently for it. They turned most often to *Genesis* and to the many commentaries which it inspired on the six days of creation. Upon such accounts, many medieval geographical concepts were based. The pagan philosopher retreated before the Christian theologue.

v *The New Wave*

O NE OF the first instances of Christian scholarship as it touched
upon the Atlantic is a work by Minucius Felix (c. A.D. 180),
a Roman lawyer and convert to Christianity, who noted the be-
nign effects of the Gulf Stream. In writing a defense of his faith
he stated: "Neither does God have care alone for the universe as
a whole, but also for its parts. Britain is deficient in sunshine, but
it is refreshed by the warmth of the sea that flows around it." [1]

Tertullian (c. 160 to 230), a Carthaginian Christian, was well
versed in classical literature and science from which he drew mu-
nitions for an anti-intellectual crusade. Was he himself interested
in the physical world and the ocean? Certainly not.

But what concern have I with physiological conceits? It were better
for one's mind to ascend above the state of the world, not to stoop down
to uncertain speculations. Plato's form of the world was round. Its
square angular shape, such as others had conceived it to be, he rounded
off, I suppose, with compasses. . . . Epicurus . . . found the sun to be a
foot in diameter. Thus far you must confess men were niggardly in even
celestial objects. In process of time their ambitious conceptions advanced, and so the sun too enlarged its disk. Accordingly, the Peri-
patetics marked it out as a larger world. Now, pray tell me, what wis-
dom is this hankering after conjectural speculations? What proof is
afforded to us notwithstanding the strong confidence of its assertions,
by the useless affectation of a scrupulous curiosity, which is tricked
out with an artful show of language? [2]

[1] Minucius Felix, *Octavius*, 18, in *Ante-Nicene Fathers*, Alexander
Roberts and James Donaldson (eds.) (New York, 1907), IV. The Latin
is "Britannia sole deficitur sed cicumfluentis maris tepore recreatur."
J. P. Migne (ed.) *Series Latina*, III, 299.

The reference to the Gulf Stream is, of course, not direct. Those in-
terested in the gradual recognition of this phenomenon might read Hans
Leip, *The River in the Sea*, (New York, 1958), 24–43, 77–89. See also
Nansen, *In Northern Mists*, II, 64; Ashe, *Land to the West*, 139–40.

[2] Tertullian, *Ad Nationes*, II, 4, trans. Peter Holmes, in *Ante-Nicene
Christian Library* (Edinburg, 1869), XI.

Tertullian's distrust of classical scholarship was matched, apparently, by his distrust of the sea: "So too, the sea has an ill repute for honesty; while at one time, the breezes equably swaying it, tranquillity gives it the semblance of probity, calm gives it the semblance of even temper; and then all of a sudden it heaves restlessly with mountain-waves."[3] He followed this last statement with a reference to the Atlantis of Plato. "In the Atlantic," he said, "the isle that was equal in size to Libya or Asia is sought in vain" because of the "vice" of the sea.[4]

In spite of his flippant reference to Plato and his compasses, Tertullian habitually referred to the earth as an orb; and, although he professed not to care, he seemed to consider the earth spherical. Many of those who transmitted ancient knowledge to the medieval world, however, took the word *orbis* in their classical texts to mean literally "circle" or "disk."

Lactantius (d. c. 325), another early Christian propagandist, had a tremendous store of classical knowledge at his disposal. He was extremely well acquainted with the systems of the early philosophers. One chapter in his principal work, *The Divine Institutions*, was concerned with the spherical earth and the antipodes. What did he think of these? The Christian pleader approached the jury:

Is there anyone so senseless as to believe that there are men whose footsteps are higher than their heads? or that the things which with us are in a recumbent position, with them hang in an inverted direction? that the crops and trees grow downward? that the rains, and snow, and hail fall upwards to the earth?[5]

He proceeded to explain how such an error had originated:

What course of argument, therefore, led them to the idea of the antipodes? They saw the courses of the stars travelling towards the west; they saw the sun and the moon always set towards the same quarter, and rise from the same. But since they did not perceive what contrivance regulated their courses, nor how they returned from the west to the east, but supposed that the heaven itself sloped downwards in every direction, which appearance it must present on account of its immense

---

[3] Tertullian, *On the Ascetics' Mantle*, II, trans. S. Thelwall in *Ante-Nicene Christian Library*, XVIII.

[4] *Ibid.*

[5] Lactantius, *The Divine Institutions*, III, 24, trans. William Fletcher, in *Ante-Nicene Christian Library*, XXI.

breadth *they thought that the world is round like a ball,* and they fancied
that the heaven revolves in accordance with the motion of the heavenly
bodies; and thus that the stars and sun, when they have set, by the very
rapidity of the motion of the world are borne back to the east. . . . It
followed, therefore, from this rotundity of the heaven, that the earth
was enclosed in the midst of its curved surface. But if this were so, the
earth also itself must be like a globe; for that could not possibly be anything but round, which was held enclosed by that which was round.
But if the earth also were round, it must necessarily happen that it should
present the same appearance to all parts of the heaven; that is, that it
should raise aloft mountains, extend plains, and have level seas. And if
this were so, that last consequence also followed that there would be no
part of the earth uninhabited by men and the other animals. Thus the
rotundity of the earth leads, in addition, to the invention of those suspended antipodes.

I am at a loss what to say respecting those who, when they have once
erred, consistently persevere in their folly, and defend one vain thing
by another; but that I sometimes imagine that they either discuss philosophy for the sake of a jest, or purposely and knowingly undertake
to defend falsehoods, as if to exercise or display their talents on false
subjects.[6]

Having disposed of the giant folly of sphericity and the marvelous fictions it produced, Lactantius turned to the Bible for truth:

Therefore, first of all, God made the heaven and suspended it on high.
. . . Then He founded the earth and placed it under the heaven. . . . He
willed that it should be surrounded and held together by water. . . .
He also established two parts of the earth itself opposite to one another,
and of a different character,—namely the east and the west; and of these
the east is assigned to God, because He Himself is the fountain of light,
and the enlightener of all things, and because He makes us rise to eternal
life. But the west is ascribed to that disturbed and depraved mind, because it conceals the light, because it always brings on darkness, and
because it makes men die and perish in their sins.[7]

He went on to describe the alliance of the south with the east
and of the north with the west. There was not any direct reference
to the Atlantic but, from its very location and his description of
the west in the passage above, we know something of how he felt
about it. He was trying to push the west back into its traditional

---

[6] *Ibid.* Italics are this author's.
[7] Lactantius, *The Divine Institutions,* II, 10.

Ptolemy's Western Ocean

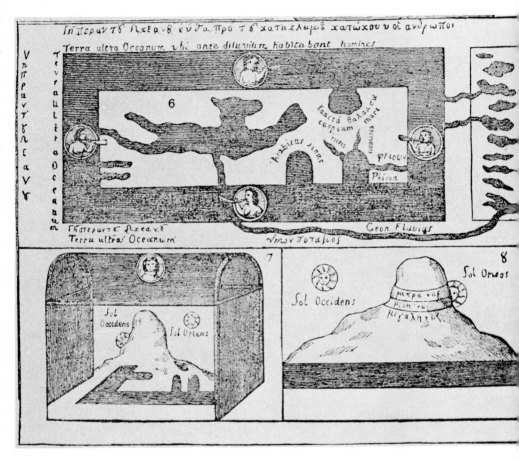

The World According to Cosmas

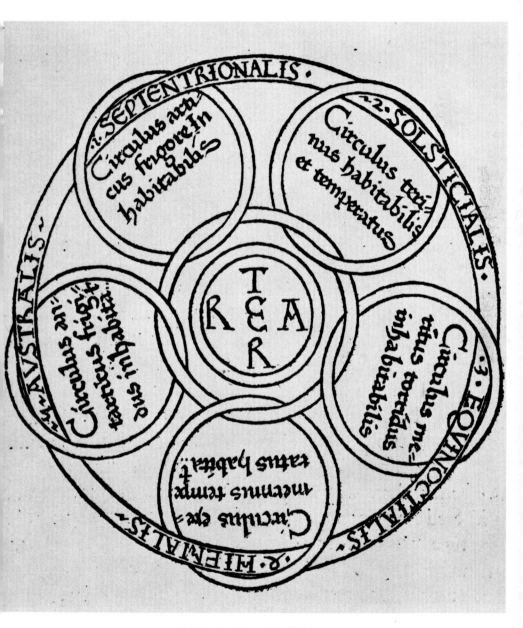

Isidore's Climatic Circles

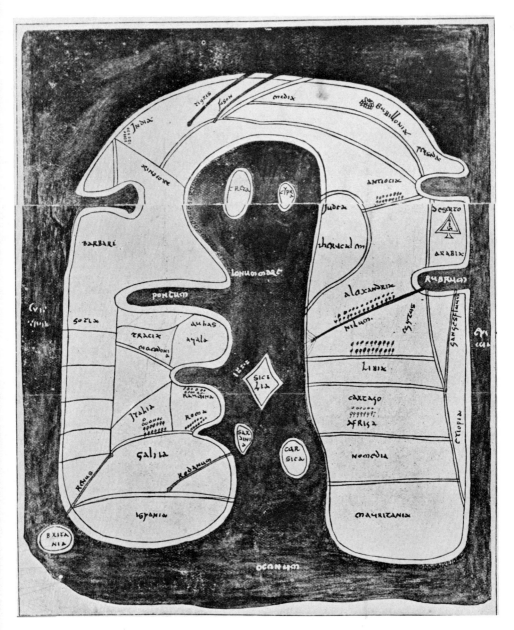

The Albi World Map

role as the abode of death; even the ancient Egyptians had "gone west" at death. Furthermore he was making the Atlantic a logical locale for the Christian Hell.

St. Basil of Caesarea (c. 375) was one of the first to write a Hexaemeron, a commentary on the six days of creation. He, just as Tertullian and Lactantius, had much knowledge of classical science, but he was not as aggressive a disputant as they. He had more trust in reason and more tolerance of divergent opinion. In matters which were not faith-shaking he was frequently willing to cite contrary opinions and not commit himself.

Basil's *Hexaemeron* was praised by his fourth-century contemporaries and remained popular through the centuries. It was imitated by St. Ambrose and many others, and was translated into Latin by Eustathius Afer (A.D. 440). Dionysius Exiguus, the sixth-century monk responsible for the A.D.-B.C. system of dating, also is supposed to have made a translation. At the end of the tenth century, Aelfric, Abbot of St. Albans (who may be identical with the more famous Aelfric, Archbishop of Canterbury from 996 to 1006), produced an Anglo-Saxon *Exameron* which apparently relied to some extent upon Basil's work.

Does the earth, Basil asked, rest in a bed of air? Unlikely. Upon water? Why doesn't it sink? And, granted it doesn't, wherein is the water contained? Does it have some more solid base? What base has the base? Curiosity carried too far was obviously fruitless and vain, so Basil concluded: "Let us then reply to ourselves and let us reply to those who ask us upon what support this enormous mass rests, 'In his hands are the ends of the earth.' It is a doctrine as infallible for our own information as profitable for our hearers." [8]

Even among the early Christians there were some who felt that the biblical word of God should supplement rather than veto scientific truth. Many of these resorted to allegorical interpretation of the Scripture. Basil attacked such people in a section in which he also discussed the shape of the earth:

There are those truly who do not admit the common sense of the Scrip-

[8] St. Basil, *Hexaemeron*, I, 9, trans. Bloomfield Jackson (New York, 1895).

tures, . . . who see in a plant, in a fish, what their fancy wishes, who change the nature of reptiles and of wild beasts to suit their allegories. . . . I take all in a literal sense. "For I am not ashamed of the gospel." [Rom. 1: 16] Those who have written about the nature of the universe have discussed at length the shape of the earth. If it be spherical or cylindrical, if it resemble a disc and is equally rounded in all parts, or if it has the form of a winnowing basket and is hollow in the middle; all these conjectures have been suggested by cosmographers, each one upsetting that of his predecessor. *It will not lead me to give less importance to the creation of the universe, that the servant of God, Moses, is silent as to shapes; . . . Shall I not rather exalt Him who, not wishing to fill our minds with these vanities, has regulated all the economy of the Scripture in view of the making perfect of our souls.*[9]

The archbishop felt that any knowledge which was not in the Bible was unnecessary. Fortunately for our search, if not for our souls, his work contained more than that.

His allusions to the Western Sea were few. One was merely a reference;[10] another concerned the lunar breath control of tides: "As to the Western sea, we see it in its ebb and flow now return into its bed, and now overflow, as the moon draws it back by her *respiration* and then, by her *expiration*, urges it to its own boundaries." [11]

Homily IV, *Upon the Gathering together of the Waters*, had a good deal of information about seas in general, including the observation that:

For fear the water should spread beyond its bed, and in its successive invasions cover one by one all countries, and end by flooding the earth, it received the order to gather unto one place. Thus we often see the furious sea raising mighty waves to the heaven, and, when once it has touched the shore, break its impetuosity in foam and retire! "Fear ye not, saith the Lord . . . which have placed the sand for the bound of the sea." [Jer. 5: 22] A grain of sand, the weakest thing possible, curbs the violence of the ocean.[12]

There was a possible problem. If water covered the whole earth, the basins which contain the seas must have been already

[9] *Ibid.*, IX, 1. Italics are this author's.
[10] *Ibid.*, III, 6.
[11] *Ibid.*, VI, 11. Italics are this author's.
[12] *Ibid.*, IV, 3.

filled and the surplus water would have no place to gather. Basil replied that this argument did not, as it were, hold water, that the basins

... were only prepared at the moment when the water had to unite in a single mass. At that time the sea which is beyond Gadeira and the vast ocean, so dreaded by navigators, which surrounds the isle of Britain and western Spain, did not exist. But all of a sudden, God created this vast space, and the mass of waters flowed in.[13]

Here then was how the Atlantic originated. St. Basil acknowledged, however, that there were those who taught of an all-surrounding ocean which would include the Atlantic. He did not reject such a belief although he carefully qualified his statements:

... there is only one sea, as those affirm who have travelled around the earth. Although some authorities think the Hyrcanian and Caspian Seas are enclosed in their own boundaries, if we are to believe the geographers, they communicate with each other and together discharge themselves into the Great Sea. It is thus that, according to their account, the Red Sea and that beyond Gadeira only form one.[14]

Some of the creatures of the sea, Basil said, were placed there to satisfy man's needs, others simply to make him marvel at the wonders of creation. Still others were made "terrible so as to take our idleness to school. . . . But these monstrous creatures do not frequent our coasts and shores; they inhabit the Atlantic Ocean." [15]

"And," said Basil, turning back to the Bible, "God saw that it was good." [16] The archbishop then proceeded to explain:

A fair sight is the sea all bright in a settled calm; fair too, when, ruffled by a light breeze of wind, its surface shows *tints of purple and azure,*—when, instead of lashing with violence the neighboring shores it seems to kiss them with peaceful caresses. However it is not in this that Scripture makes God find the goodness and charm of the sea. Here it is the purpose of the work which makes the goodness.[17]

In the first place, Basil wrote, the ocean was the source of all of

[13] *Ibid.*, IV, 4.
[14] *Ibid.*
[15] *Ibid.*, VII, 6. This entire passage concerns the various types of fish and animal life to be found in the Atlantic.
[16] *Genesis* 1:10.
[17] St. Basil, *Hexaemeron*, IV, 6. Italics are this author's.

the moisture in the earth. It penetrated the land in subterranean canals from which it rose until it broke through the earth's surface pure and fresh having become "free from bitterness by this long percolation." Secondly, it was the source of the moisture in the air. Vaporized by the sun the moisture rose until, cooled, it formed rain and returned to "fatten" the earth. As an example and proof of fresh water coming in this fashion from the sea, Basil informed those who were incredulous that: "Sailors, too, boil even sea water, collecting the vapour in sponges, to quench their thirst in pressing need." [18] "Finally," he pointed out:

the sea is good in the eyes of God, because it girdles the isles, of which it forms at the same time the rampart and the beauty, because it brings together the most distant parts of the earth, and facilitates the intercommunication of mariners. By this means it gives us the boon of general information, supplies the merchant with his wealth, and easily provides for the necessities of life, — allowing the rich to export their superfluities and blessing the poor with the supply of what they lack.[19]

The picture presented by St. Ambrose (d. 397) in his *Hexaemeron* did not differ essentially from that of St. Basil. He opined that there was one encircling ocean with many gulfs or "seas." His chapter on the Atlantic was primarily concerned with animal and vegetable life most of which verged on the marvelous.[20] Ambrose, too, pointed out that speculating upon the nature and placement of the earth was no step toward salvation. It is sufficient to know, he wrote, that the Bible says "He hung up the earth upon nothing." [21]

The last two books of St. Augustine's *Confessions* were a commentary upon the first chapter of *Genesis*. In his commentary, however, Augustine seldom got down to earth and was concerned with the ocean only for its mystic and allegorical significance.[22] For our investigative purposes the *City of God* is more rewarding. Here Augustine explained the sea as it appeared in

---

[18] *Ibid.*, IV, 6–7.

[19] *Ibid.*, IV, 7.

[20] Ambrose, *Hexaemeron*, III, 1–5; V, 11, in *Series Latina*, XIV, ed. J. P. Migne (Paris, 1882).

[21] *Ibid.*, I, 6. See *Job* 26:7.

[22] St. Augustine (Aurelius Augustinus), *Confessions*, XII, XIII, trans. Edward B. Pusey (New York, 1949).

the *Book of Revelation* as a symbol of "the surgings and restlessness of human life." [23] But more than that, he made several pronouncements which were especially important because of the great respect with which his words were received.

"Who," Augustine asked, "can doubt that, as the human races increased, men contrived to pass to the islands on ships?" Who, indeed? That is certainly no problem. But how did wolves and other animals get to remote oceanic islands after the deluge, which killed all animal life save that which was aboard the ark? Augustine knew of three possibilities. Men, fond of the chase, might have brought them; angels, with God's permission, might have spirited them there; they might have been re-created, produced from the earth, on those spots. Augustine considered the last possibility most likely.[24]

What about certain "monstrous races of men, spoken of in secular history," those with dog's heads, pigmies, one-legged men with feet large enough to serve as umbrellas, men with no heads? Here too the answer was manifold. Maybe, Augustine said hopefully, they did not all really exist; perhaps some were beasts that had been mistaken for men. However, no Christian could doubt his kinship through Noah, with anyone who was "anywhere born a man, that is a rational mortal animal, no matter what unusual appearance he presents in colour, movement, sound, nor how peculiar he is in some power, part or quality of his nature." [25]

What about the antipodal regions where such strange people were frequently reported to live? At this Augustine balked: "But as to the fable that there are Antipodes, that is to say, men on the opposite side of the earth, where the sun rises when it sets to us, men who walk with their feet opposite ours, that is on no ground credible." [26] Lactantius would have been delighted. Augustine continued:

And indeed, it is not affirmed that this has been learned by historical knowledge, but by scientific conjecture, on the ground that the earth is suspended within the concavity of the sky, and that it has as much

[23] St. Augustine, *City of God*, XX, 16, trans. Marcus Dods (New York, 1950).

[24] *Ibid.*, XVI, 6–7.

[25] *Ibid.*, XVI, 8.

[26] *Ibid.*, XVI, 9.

room on the one side of it as on the other; hence they say that the part which is beneath must also be inhabited.[27]

Though at first this sounds like a paraphrase of Lactantius, there suddenly comes a difference. Augustine not only suggested that the earth might be spherical but went on to suggest that the under part of the earth might be covered with water. He concluded, "although it be supposed or scientifically demonstrated that the world is of a round and spherical form, yet it does not follow that the other side of the earth is bare of water; nor even, though it be bare, does it immediately follow that it is peopled.[28] Furthermore, if there were people there they would have to be descended from Adam. This Augustine ruled out for two reasons. "Scripture," he said, "gives no false information." To this one might respond that St. Basil had pointed out that much truth unnecessary to salvation had been omitted. Furthermore, Augustine said, "it is too absurd to say that some men might have taken ship and traversed the whole wide ocean, and crossed from this side of the world to the other, and that thus even the inhabitants of that distant region are descended from that one first man." [29]

[27] *Ibid.*
[28] *Ibid.*
[29] *Ibid.*

VI *Oceans of Faith*

Paulus Orosius, a Spanish theologian, was a friend and disciple of St. Augustine and the author of *Seven Books of History Against the Pagans*. This work was a favorite in the Middle Ages. The geographical treatise with which Orosius began his history is therefore important, not for anything new, but because it contained much that was to remain familiar and accepted. As we shall see, it was one of the books which Alfred the Great felt should be translated into Anglo-Saxon for the instruction of his clergy.

Orosius' world was surrounded on its periphery by the ocean. North and east of Europe was the Sarmatian sea; to the west, the Western ocean which also bordered upon Africa. Off the African coast were "the islands which people call Fortunate." In the northern Atlantic were Britain, extending "a long distance to the north"; the Orcades, "in the *limitless* ocean which stretches beyond Britain"; Ireland, "an island situated between Britain and Spain"; Mevania (Man), "its next door neighbor"; and, beyond the Orkneys, "the island of Thule, which is separated from the others by a great space and is situated in the middle of the Ocean toward the northwest, it is known to only a few." [1]

One other section of the history might be noted in passing. In his sixth book Orosius observed:

Thus Rome's fortune . . . may be compared to the level of the Ocean, which is never the same from day to day. For a space of seven days the level rises by increases that gradually grow less, and then in the same number of days falls as a result of natural loss and internal absorption. [2]

[1] Paulus Orosius, *Seven Books of History Against the Pagans*, I, 2, trans. I. W. Raymond (New York, 1936). Italics are this author's.
[2] *Ibid.*, VI, 14.

The moon would seem to have lost its influence on the ocean.

Once again we turn to Carthage for an informant. Martianus Capella apparently lived and wrote in North Africa sometime before this region was occupied by the Vandals. This Latin writer, although possibly a contemporary of St. Augustine, was apparently untouched by Christianity. He was, nevertheless, to become mentor to many during the Middle Ages. His *Marriage of Philology and Mercury*, an encyclopaedic work, was frequently used as a school text during the medieval period.[3]

After an introductory allegory from which the work receives its title, Martianus Capella devoted one book to each of the seven liberal arts. The sixth book, which dealt with geometry, included much geographical material with emphasis upon its mathematical aspects.

According to Capella, the earth was spherical. He presented his readers with those proofs suggested by, among others, Aristotle and Pliny. His figure, 252,000 stades, for the circumference of the earth was that of Eratosthenes. He divided the earth into the traditional five zones and limited life to the north and south temperate zones, postulating four inhabited land masses: one below the equator and the known world, two others across the Atlantic in the northern and southern hemispheres.[4]

The other three inhabited land masses could only be known through theory. Capella claimed, concerning his own world, to be on surer ground. He cited Ptolemy's geographical treatise as a source, referred to Pytheas' account of Thule, and, furthermore, claimed to have traveled widely himself.[5] The ocean, he maintained, was navigable around the known world. The possibility of circumnavigation had been proved to his satisfaction by the voyage of the fleet of Augustus in the north; in the east by Macedonians—during the reigns of Seleucus and Antiochus—who reputedly sailed from the Indian Ocean to the Caspian Sea; and in

---

[3] Martianus Capella, *De Nuptiis Philologiae et Mercurii*, ed. F. Eyssenhardt (Leipzig, 1865). See William H. Stahl, "To a Better Understanding of Martianus Capella," *Speculum*, XL (1965), 102–15.

[4] Capella, *De Nuptiis*, VI, 590–98, 602–608.

[5] *Ibid.*, VI, 595, 609, 610, 616, 666.

the south and west by exploration carried out by ships of Alexander the Great, by wrecks reported during the reign of Caligula to have drifted around Africa to Asia, and by the circumnavigatory voyages of Hanno, Eudoxus, and an unknown merchant.[6] This list was concluded with what was obviously a reference to the Indians blown by storm from India to captivity in Germany. All of the above was condensed from Pliny's *Natural History*.[7] In fact, it appears that for the remaining section on geography, the far-traveler had traveled no farther than to the nearest copies of Pliny and Solinus.

Capella followed Pliny in placing the mythical happy Hyperboreans at the top of the earth and beyond the north wind, although this did not fit in with the picture he had presented earlier of habitable and non-habitable zones.[8] In the Atlantic off the coast of Europe, in addition to the British islands (Ireland was not mentioned), he had "Ultima Tyle" and beyond it the congealed or frozen sea. Off the African coast he placed the Gorgades, the Hesperides, and the Fortunate Islands.[9]

Cicero's *On the Commonwealth* included a passage on the "Dream of Scipio." A well-known commentary on the passage was written by Macrobius, a contemporary of Capella. The birthplace of Macrobius is unknown. He, too, may have been an African, and he may have been an official under Theodosius. He may or may not have been a Christian, but his *Commentary on the Dream of Scipio* rivaled Capella's *Marriage of Philology and Mercury* in popularity during the Middle Ages.[10]

Macrobius presented much the same theoretical world picture to the Middle Ages as did Capella. A spherical earth, divided into

---

[6] *Ibid.,* VI, 618–21.

[7] Pliny, *Natural History*, II, 67.

[8] Capella, *De Nuptiis*, VI, 664. Cf. Pliny, *Natural History*, IV, 12.

[9] *Ibid.,* VI, 666, 702. Cf. Ashe, *Land to the West*, 137.

[10] Stahl says in the introduction to his translation of Macrobius' *Commentary on the Dream of Scipio*, 39: "It is not difficult to account for the great popularity of Macrobius' *Commentary* in the Middle Ages. Perhaps no other book of comparably small size contained so many subjects of interest and doctrines that are repeatedly found in medieval literature." Macrobius, *Commentary on the Dream of Scipio*, II, 5, 9, trans. William Stahl (New York, 1952).

five zones, with the northern and southern temperate zones inhabitable. In each of these temperate zones there were two continental land masses separated from each other by ocean and fiery equator, with no possibility of intercommunication.[11] There might, however, be people living there, and it was foolish to think that people living below the equator would fall off. It has been aptly noted that Macrobius supported the scientific tradition of terrestrial gravitation "by charmingly circular arguments of his own." [12] He followed Eratosthenes' calculation of 252,000 stades for the circumference of the earth.[13]

Macrobius pointed out that the ocean in its ebb and flow coincided with phases of the moon. However, his account did not indicate that the latter influenced the former but rather that they were both influenced by the number seven.[14] The mechanics of the tidal phenomenon received considerable attention:

> That Ocean which is generally supposed to be the only one is really a secondary body, a great circle which was obliged to branch off from the original body. The main course actually flows around the earth's torrid zone, girdling our hemisphere and the underside, and follows the circumference of the equator. In the east it divides, one stream flowing off to the northern extremity, the other to the southern; likewise in the west, streams flow to the north and south, where they meet the streams from the east at the poles. As they rush together with great violence and impetus and buffet each other, the impact produces the remarkable ebb and flow of Ocean.[15]

We have already mentioned that the fifth-century grammarian Priscian translated the work of Dionysius Periegetes and thus ensured its continued popularity throughout the Middle Ages. Both he and Avienus, who also translated the *Periegesis*, treated the original loosely but, Beazley points out: "neither added much to the current misconceptions, except a welcome confirmation." [16]

[11] *Ibid.*
[12] C. R. Beazley, *Dawn of Modern Geography* (London, 1897), I, 344.
[13] Macrobius, *Commentary*, II, 6.
[14] *Ibid.*, I, 6, lxi.
[15] *Ibid.*, II, 9, i–iii.
[16] Beazley, *Dawn of Modern Geography*, I, 364. Priscian's *Interpretatio Ex Dionysio de Orbe Situ* also may be found in Priscian, *Opera*, ed. Augustus Krehl (Liepzig, 1820), II.

In rejecting much of the scientific knowledge and speculation of classical scholarship, the early Christians tended to favor many concepts which were in accord with the less scientific views of the Homeric and earlier periods: the flat earth surrounded by ocean, the sea of darkness, and death in the west. They also accelerated a tendency, already apparent in the writings of Pliny and Solinus, to neglect the commonplace facts of nature and emphasize the marvelous, the miraculous, and the legendary. Moreover, the Christian world-viewer delighted in real or imagined symmetry, whether intra-geographical or extra-geographical: the four cardinal points of the compass represented the four gospels; the three continents, the three sons of Noah; and *ad infinitum*. All these tendencies were evident in the *Christian Topography* of Cosmas Indicopleustes (A.D. 550). This particular work is an example of what a "dedicated" Christian might do with the resources at hand.

Cosmas had seen much of the world and had traveled extensively in the Far East as a merchant, but he distrusted the testimony of his senses. He became a monk and accepted Holy Writ as wholly right in matters of both faith and fact. Those geographical ideas which he felt were contrary to Scripture he declared false. His earth, modeled after the tabernacle, was twice as long as it was broad,[17] and, when he read in the *Book of Revelation* that John saw four angels standing on the four corners of the earth, he put down his compasses and picked up a straight edge.[18]

The cosmos of Cosmas revealed the earth as a rectangular plane at the bottom of the universe. It was God's footstool. The earth was surrounded by an ocean and this ocean by another earth which had been the home of mankind prior to the flood. In the north on this other earth there was a mountain the shadow of which, when the sun passed behind it, caused the night.[19]

Cosmas frequently cited ancient authorities whose arguments seemed to strengthen his own. His account of the earth beyond the ocean contains an allusion to the Atlantis of Plato, which he ascribed to the "philosopher Timaeus":

[17] *Exodus* 37:10 and *Hebrews* 9:23–24.

[18] *Revelation*, 7:1.

[19] Cosmas Indicopleustes, *Christian Topography*, trans. J. W. McCrindle (London, 1897), 33, 376.

. . . for men continued to live in the earth beyond [the Ocean] 2242 years for a course of ten generations, and under Noah who was the tenth the flood having occurred, they passed over to this earth by means of the Ark. . . . In like manner the philosopher Timaeus also describes this earth as surrounded by the Ocean, and the Ocean as surrounded by the more remote earth. For he supposes that there is to westward an island, Atlantis, lying out in the Ocean, in the direction of Gadeira [Cadiz], of an enormous magnitude, and relates that the ten kings having procured mercenaries from the nations in this island came from the earth far away and conquered Europe and Asia, but were afterwards conquered by the Athenians, while the island itself was submerged by God under the sea.[20]

Cosmas explained the sinking of Atlantis as a garbled account of the biblical deluge, hopelessly obscured by invention:

Timaeus . . . recast the story of those ten kings, feigning that they came from the earth beyond the Ocean into the island of Atlantis, which he says was submerged below the sea, and that taking its inhabitants as mercenaries, and arriving in this earth, they conquered Europe and Asia—all which is a most manifest invention, for as he could not point out the island, he gave out that God had consigned it to a watery grave.[21]

Included in a ninth-century Florentine manuscript of the *Christian Topography*, there were some sketches which may date from the time of Cosmas himself.[22] If so, these are probably the oldest Christian maps that have survived. Unfortunately, except for the square corners, they were completely lacking in detail concerning the Atlantic.

A Christian Goth named Jordanes wrote the *Getica*, a history of his people, in the middle of the sixth century. He purported to be condensing a history of the Goths by Cassiodorus, now lost, which he had read twice in the past and did not then have at hand. He had also, he said in his preface, "added fitting matters from some Greek and Latin histories" and inserted many things of his own authorship. In his geographical introduction he referred to Orosius, Virgil, Tacitus, Mela, Dio Cassius, and Ptolemy.

[20] *Ibid.*, 375–76.
[21] *Ibid.*, 380.
[22] Beazley, *Dawn of Modern Geography*, I, 384.

The truth of Jordanes' statement has been challenged with regard both to the book he did not have at hand and to the ones he claimed to have used. It has been suggested that he denied having the history by Cassiodorus at his fingertips to hide his own lack of originality, that the book contained long literal excerpts from the work of Cassiodorus, and that Jordanes' Latin became worse when he ceased to copy.[23]

There were echoes of much familiar material in the *Getica*. The tripartite earth of Jordanes was surrounded (at least on three sides) by ocean, the entire coast of which was known and inhabited by men.[24] Also supporting human life were many islands in the "vast flood of the sea." Thus far knowledge extended, he wrote, but "the impassable farther bounds of Ocean not only has no one attempted to describe, but no man has been allowed to

[23] Nansen, *In Northern Mists*, I, 130.

[24] Jordanes, *The Origin and Deeds of the Goths*, I, 4, trans. Charles C. Mierow (Princeton, 1908). However, there is a minor problem here. The Latin text of Jordanes' *Getica*, edited by Theodor Mommsen in *M. G. H., Auctores Antiquissimi*, V, Pt. 1 (Berlin, 1882) has: "Maiores nostri, ut refert Orosius, totius terrae circulum Oceani limbo circumseptum triquadrum statuerunt eiusque tres partes Asiam, Europam et Africam vocaverunt."

Mierow's translation is: "Our ancestors, as Orosius relates, were of the opinion that the circle of the whole world was surrounded by the girdle of Ocean *on three sides*." This translation appears to be quite justified but at the same time a bit startling. This statement, Jordanes says, is from Orosius, which is quite true. Orosius had said in his *History*, I, 2, i: "Majores nostri orbem totius terrae Oceani limbo circumseptum triquadrum statuere: ejusterae tres partes Asiam, Europam et Africam vocaverunt." Raymond translates this: "Our elders made a *threefold* division of the world, which is surrounded on its periphery by the Ocean. Its three parts they named Asia, Europe, and Africa." This is certainly what Orosius meant, but his statement also can be translated differently. One wonders if others before Mierow misinterpreted either his text or that of Jordanes and ended up with an ocean on three sides.

King Alfred did not. In his translation (itself translated by this author), he has: "Our elders divided all the orb of this middle-earth, which is encircled by the ocean that is called Spearman, into three. . . ."

Nor can we find any indication of this variant translation elsewhere; yet the theory was soon to appear, e.g. the Ravennese geographer, that the ocean only bordered the earth on the north, west, and south, and on the fourth side was Paradise.

reach: for by reason of obstructing seaweed and the failing of the winds it is plainly inaccessible and is unknown to any save to him who made it." [25]

Jordanes' cataloging of islands in the Atlantic was somewhat confused although he said that they were "known to almost everyone by reason of the great number of those that journey to and fro." Thule was placed at the farthest bounds of the western expanse of the ocean; Britain, as Tacitus had written, was surrounded by a sluggish sea. The ocean to the extreme north was described as vast and unnavigable.[26]

Jordanes' Thule, far to the west, was definitely not Scandinavia, about which he or his source had some firsthand information (possibly from northern troops serving the Byzantines).[27] On the other hand, the Byzantine historian Procopius of Caesarea (c. 525), who also knew much about Scandinavia, probably from the same or a similar source, definitely equated Thule with Norway. His Thule was exceedingly large, ten times greater than Britain, and farther to the north.[28]

In another reference, however, Procopius did show some doubt as to Thule's placement. The mysterious country, he said, "as far as men know at any rate is situated towards the extremity of the northern ocean." Britain was off the "extreme end" of Spain and above it "towards the rear of Gaul" there was another island, called Brittia, inhabited by "three very numerous nations," the Angili, the Frissones, and Brittones. Brittia would appear to have been occupied by much the same people as Britain. Nor did the resemblance stop there. In ancient times the men of Brittia "built a long wall, cutting off a large part of it," Procopius reported. Brittia was Britain; or, rather, Britain had become two islands. The new Britain had some strange characteristics. The historical purpose of the wall across the island had apparently been forgotten. Procopius explained that "the climate and the soil and everything else is not alike on the two sides of it." The west side was

[25] Jordanes, *Getica*, I, 5–6.

[26] *Ibid.*, I, 7, 9, 12, 17.

[27] Cf. Nansen, *In Northern Mists*, I, 138.

[28] Procopius, *History of the Wars*, VI, 15, iv–xxvi, trans. H. B. Dewing (New York, 1919).

the abode of death and it was "actually impossible for a man to survive there even a half-hour." [29]

Procopius continued:

They say, then, that the souls of men who die are always conveyed to this place [Brittia]. And as to the manner in which this is done, I shall presently explain, having many a time heard the people there most earnestly describe it, though I have come to the conclusion that the tales they tell are to be attributed to some power of dreams. Along the coast of the ocean which lies opposite the island of Brittia there are numerous villages. These are inhabited by men who fish with nets or till the soil or carry on a sea-trade with this island.

The men of this place say that the conduct of souls is laid upon them. . . . And at a late hour of the night they are conscious of a knocking at their doors and hear an indistinct voice calling them . . . to the shore. . . . There they see skiffs in readiness with no man at all in them . . . in which they embark and lay hold of the oars. And they are aware that the boats are burdened with a large number of passengers and are wet by the waves to the edge of the planks and the oarlocks, having not so much as one finger's breadth above the water; they themselves, however, see no one, but after rowing a single hour they put in at Brittia. And yet . . . in their own skiffs, not using sails but rowing, they with difficulty make this passage in a night and a day. Then . . . relieved of their burden, they depart with all speed, their boats now becoming suddenly light and rising above the waves, for they sink no further in the water than the keel itself.[30]

This seems to be, with considerable embellishment, the tale told earlier by Claudian that on the furthermost shore of Gaul could be heard the mournful weeping of the souls of the dead.

A cosmographical work ascribed to Aethicus of Istria (and dating back at least to the seventh century) has been proclaimed "one of the longest, one of the wildest, and certainly the most obscure and enigmatical among early Christian monuments." [31] Aethicus was quite sure of the encircling ocean. In fact he claimed to have sailed most of it personally and encountered a good many marvels on the way. Some of his less spectacular islands included Ireland, the Orkneys, Britain, and Thule. Far to the north, he reported,

---

[29] *Ibid.*, VIII, 20, iv–xlv.
[30] *Ibid.*, VIII, 20, xlviii–lv.
[31] Beazley, *Dawn of Modern Geography*, I, 355.

there were people who were advanced in the arts of music, war, and navigation.[32] Furthermore, Alexander the Great had visited these northern navigators, and while there he had even managed to explore the bottom of the sea.[33]

About A.D. 650, a now anonymous scholar of Ravenna attempted a description of the world. He appears to have known Greek, to have been acquainted with Ptolemy, with several lost Gothic cosmographies, with some Roman itineraries and maps, and with a wide range of other sources. He also seems to have profited little from them. The map supposed to accompany the text has been lost. As reconstructed by d'Avezac, the map showed an oblong world completely surrounded by water, with Paradise depicted in the ocean to the east.[34] This last point, however, is not justified by the text, which seems to indicate the earth had three sides bordered by seas with Paradise on the fourth side.[35]

The Ravennese geographer considered the ocean west and north of Britain to be impassable. Therefore men might never see the mountain on its farther side which nightly hid the sun. Some islands within the ocean might be reached, he conjectured; among these, in addition to the British Isles, were the Fortunate Islands and apparently two Thules—one northeast of Britain and another off the coast of Spain.[36]

---

[32] Aethicus, *Die Kosmographie des Istrier Aithikos*, XXV–XXVII, XXXI, ed. Heinrich Wuttke (Leipzig, 1853).

[33] *Ibid.*, XXXVI: "Aiunt enim in ipsas colimfas ipsum Alexandrum introisse et in profundum maris discendisse usque ad imum, ut sciret oceani profundum et differentiam maris et abyssi sciret; nobis vero incredibile videtur."

A *colimpha*, according to Du Cange in *Glossarium Mediae Infimae Latinitatis*, is a *Navicula Urinatoria*, which, happily, is a diving bell. Incidentally, Varro, *De Langua Latina*, V, 126, explains the connection. Re Alexander, see De Latil and Rivoire, *Man and the Underwater World*, 79–84.

[34] Appended to M. A. P. d'Avezac-Macaya, *Le Ravennate et son Exposé Cosmographique* (Rouen, 1888).

[35] Cf. Nansen, *In Northern Mists*, I, 153.

[36] *Ravennatis Anonymi Cosmographia*, ed. M. Pinder and G. Parthey (Berlin, 1860). Re Britain and "Thile," see chapter 31; re Fortunate Islands and "Thyle," see chapter 33.

VII *On the Rim of the Wheel*

ISIDORE, the well-read Bishop of Seville (c. 625), was the author of an encyclopaedic work, *The Etymologies*, which would be relied upon as a source of information for the next six hundred years. Isidore culled from both pagan and patristic sources for an orthodox Christian audience. He did not always understand his originals and perhaps at times he chose deliberately to reinterpret them.

The earth, he wrote, was called *orbis* because it was like a wheel with the ocean flowing all around it.[1] His, therefore, was a flat and circular earth. He also used other terms which applied to a spherical world, but it is not difficult to decide which set of expressions was meaningless to him, especially if one turns to another work of his, the *De Natura Rerum*. "In describing the world," he said, "philosophers affirm [there are] five circles, which the Greeks call zones, into which the orb of the earth is divided."[2] Eratosthenes would have nodded assent, but only to the initial statement. In the first place, one must remember that "orb" can mean wheel. Isidore, taking *zona* and *circulus* to be interchangeable, laid these five climatic circles flat and side by side around the circle of a flat earth. The equinoctial circle to the south was described as burnt by the sun and uninhabitable. Above

[1] Isidore, *Etymologiae*, XIV, 2, 1, ed. W. M. Lindsay (Oxford, 1911). This work is very ably analyzed and to a large extent translated by Ernest Brehaut, *An Encyclopaedist of the Dark Ages, Isidore of Seville* (New York, 1912). The English translations of passages from the *Etymologiae* are from Brehaut. See also Jacques Fontaine, "Isidore de Seville et la mutation de l'Encyclopédisme Antique," *Journal of World History*, IX (1966), 519–38.

[2] Isidore, *De Natura Rerum*, X, 1, in *Series Latina*, LXXXIII, ed. J. P. Migne (Paris, 1862): "In definitione autem mundi circulos aiunt philosophi quinque, quos Graeci zonas vocant, in quibus dividitur orbis terrae."

it, to the east and west, were the two temperate zones. Above these were the Arctic and Antarctic circles which, "adjacent to each other, are not inhabited since they are far removed from the course of the sun." [3]

In both the *Etymologiae* and *De Natura Rerum*, Isidore dealt with many familiar problems concerning the sea. The treatment is the same in both works.[4]

Although rivers and streams were forever flowing into the sea, it did not overflow. Isidore explained that this was due to the sea's vastness; the ocean was so great that such waters made little impression upon it. He also offered an alternative explanation:

. . . because the bitter water consumes the fresh that is added, or that the clouds draw up much water to themselves, or that the winds carry it off, and the sun partly dries it up; lastly, because the water leaks through certain secret holes in the earth, and turns and runs back to the sources of rivers and to springs.[5]

Isidore, as the title of his work suggests, was interested in the etymology of the word Oceanus, which he said was so named by both Greeks and Latins because "it flows like a circle around the circle of the land; it may be from its speed because it runs swiftly (*ocius*); or because like the heavens it glows with a dark purple color." [6]

Oceanic tides had been explained as the breathing of the earth, or as the breathing of the moon. Isidore felt they were accounted for simply by the breath of wind: "For when the winds breathe in the depth, it either pushes the waters away or sucks them back." Elsewhere he included an account of the abyss but did not, as some later authors, connect this with the tides. His explanation was reminiscent of Pliny, but it also had biblical justification. Abyssus, he wrote, was "the impenetrable deep of the waters, or

---

[3] Isidore, *ibid.*, X, 1–4.

[4] These chapters in *De Natura Rerum* are: XL, "De Oceano"; XLI, "Cur mare non crescat"; XLII, "Quare mare salsam habeat aquam"; XLV, "De positione terrae"; XLVIII, "De partibus terrae." The same is true of Isidore's *De Ordine Creaturarum*, ed. J. P. Migne (Paris, 1862): IX, "De natura aquarum et cursu Oceani"; XI, "De situ orbis terrarum, quem inhabitat genus humanum."

[5] Isidore, *Etymologiae*, XIII, 14.

[6] *Ibid.*, XIII, 15.

the caves of the hidden waters, from whence springs and rivers issue forth, but also those which run concealed beneath the ground." [7]

Isidore also described the various parts of the earth: Asia (with Paradise in the east), Europe, Africa, and a fourth part of the world across the ocean to the south which was unknown to men "on account of the sun in whose boundaries, according to story, the Antipodes are said to dwell." His qualifying remarks kept him within the bounds of orthodoxy. This was after all only a legend. He had shown less caution in an earlier section on men and monsters, stating quite positively that "The Antipodes in Libya have feet turned backward and eight toes on each foot." [8]

In addition to these land masses, there were islands. There was Britain, of course, and separated from it by a narrow strait was the island of Thanatos, "with fields rich in grain and a fertile soil." Here Isidore had a problem. Why was such an island called "death?" One might expect a Procopian account of spirits and fishermen but Isidore had seized upon another clue. The solution was simple: "It is called Thanatos from the death of snakes." [9]

His "Thyle," the "furthest island in the ocean," was located to the north and west of Britain. The remainder of Isidore's commentary on Thule had a familiar ring but made rather enigmatic etymology. He explained Thule as "having its name from the sun, because there the sun makes its summer halt, and there is no day beyond it; whence the sea there is sluggish and frozen." [10]

Also in the Atlantic were the Orchades, a snake-free Hibernia, and Gades—all off the coast of Europe—and the Fortunate Islands, the Gorgades, and the Hesperides off the coast of Africa. The Fortunate Islands, Isidore pointed out, were so fertile and fruitful that in times past they were mistakenly reputed to be Paradise.[11]

---

[7] *Ibid.*, XIII, 15; XIII, 20.

[8] *Ibid.*, XIV, 3, ii–iii; XIV, 5, xvii; XI, 3, xxiv.

[9] *Ibid.*, XIV, 6, iii.

[10] *Ibid.*, XIV, 6, iv.

[11] *Ibid.*, XIV, 6, v–x. Before leaving Isidore it might be worthwhile noting another section of the *Etymologiae* which is tangential to our interest although slightly beyond the scope of this study. Book XIX, 1–6, has to do with the construction of ships. Those interested might see also

The Venerable Bede (673–735) had much to say about the ocean. His testimony favored a spherical earth and an uninhabited antipodal area. Bede divided the world into five zones and, unlike Isidore, understood what was meant by zone. He bowed to the teachings of the Church Fathers and classified the northern temperate zone as inhabited and the southern as "habitable." [12] He recognized the lunar effect upon the tides, gave the traditional reasons for the sea not overflowing, and explained that the ocean was bitter because the sun draws up the sweet water and leaves the dross. [13]

Among the ocean islands Bede mentioned was Thule, where a prolonged day and night alternated, and which he located far to the north near the Riphean Mountains, one day's sail south of the congealed sea. [14]

Much that Bede presented was a cautious and considered repetition of his sources. On the question of tides, however, he made a notable contribution. Many scholars living in countries next to the Atlantic failed to realize that they were in a more favorable position to know the ocean than their Mediterranean counterparts. A few did. Among these was the untraveled and yet most cosmopolitan monk of Jarrow. In the *De Temporum Ratione*, Bede clearly stated for the first time the principle that tides can only

---

one of Isidore's sources, Nonius Marcellus (fourth century), *Conpendiosa Doctrina ad Filium*, Book XIII of which is "De Genere Navigiorum." Isidore would be often copied. A notable instance would be Rabanus Maurus, *De Universo*, in *Series Latina*, CXI, ed. J. P. Migne (Paris, 1852), who follows Isidore so closely there is little need of repeating all he has to say. The sections of especial interest in his *De Universo* are XI, 2, "De Mari"; XI, 3, "De Oceano"; XI, 6, "De Abysso"; XII, 1, "De Terra"; XII, 2, "De Orbe"; XII, 5, "De Insulis"; XIII, 16, "De Navalibus." We might note that in XII, 2, he tries to "square" his circular world (to him, as to Isidore, the earth is a wheel) with biblical authority. He says that if one were to draw two straight lines from the east, one to the south, and one to the north, and then in the same way draw lines from west to north and west to south, the result would be a square within a circle. This, which he adds reassuringly is demonstrated in Euclid's *Elements of Geometry*, proves there is no contradiction involved.

[12] Bede, *De Natura Rerum*, IX, XLVI, in *Series Latina*, XC, ed. J. P. Migne (Paris, 1862).

[13] *Ibid.*, XXXIX, XL, XLI; Bede, *De Temporum Ratione*, XXIX, in *Series Latina*, XC, ed. J. P. Migne (Paris, 1862).

[14] Bede, *De Natura Rerum*, XLVII, IX.

be tabulated for the individual port. Bede gave his fellow monks credit for this observation. It is true that the monks of Lindisfarne, for example, would certainly have had an interest in the tides, but Bede himself was probably responsible for the conclusion that tides could be calculated using the 19-year lunar cycle. The tidal tables which frequently appear in later *computi* may even be based upon his achievement.[15]

With Bede's exposition connecting the tides directly to lunar influence, it would seem that this point at least would have been acknowledged as settled. But such was not the case. A rival theory was championed by Paul the Deacon in the eighth century. In the opening pages of his *History of the Langobards*, Paul conceived of the Western Ocean as limitless and its tides as being caused by a great whirlpool not far from the coast of Europe. This whirlpool, he said, was the "navel of the sea":

This is said to suck the waves and spew them forth twice every day, as is proved to be done by the excessive swiftness with which the waves advance and recede along all those shores. A whirlpool or maelstrom of this kind is called by the poet Virgil "charybdis" [*Aeneid*, VII, 420]. . . . Ships are alleged to be often violently and swiftly dragged in by this whirlpool. . . . They say there is another whirlpool of this kind between the island of Britian and the province of Galicia.[16]

Many later writers would find such an explanation much more plausible than lunar influence.

Dicuil, the Irish monk and scholar who wrote the *De Mensura Orbis Terrae* in 825, occasionally, just as Bede, challenged earlier authorities when he felt that their statements were unreasonable or based on insufficient evidence. Pliny had reported, for example, that a certain Fabian said the greatest depth of the sea was two miles.[17]

[15] C. W. Jones (ed.), *Bedae Opera de Temporibus* (Cambridge, 1943), 126. The *De Mundi Coelestis Terrestrisque Constitutione* attributed to Bede in Migne and elsewhere was apparently compiled in the ninth century. It leans heavily upon Bede's *De Natura Rerum* and *De Temporum Ratione* but also reflects some works unknown to him. It does not, however, contribute anything to this investigation. See C. W. Jones, *Bedae Pseudepigrapha* (Ithaca, 1939), 85.

[16] Paul the Deacon, *History of the Langobards*, I, vi, trans. William Dudley Foulke (Philadelphia, 1907).

[17] Pliny, *Natural History*, II, 224.

Had Fabian measured the depth of every sea?, Dicuil asked. If he had not, why should his word not be challenged? [18] In most cases, however, his authorities had to go to the greatest extremes before Dicuil felt their statements unreasonable, and in some cases he even preferred their testimony when his own firsthand knowledge was undoubtedly much superior.[19]

A ninth-century Irish scholar, John Scot Erigena, used a wide range of sources in compiling his principal work, *De Divisione Naturae*, but followed, nevertheless, the usual traditions.[20] Erigena also wrote a commentary on Capella's *The Marriage of Mercury and Philology* in which he championed the belief in an inhabited antipodal continent to the south as well as the two other continental land masses originally hypothesized by Crates of Mallus.[21] His wording in this instance was quite clear. However, Erigena ap-

[18] Dicuil, *De Mensura*, VIII, 25. "Plinius Secundus in tertio libro: altissimum mare XV stadiorum Fabianus tradit sed quis credet Fabianum totius profunditatem oceani posse scire?"

[19] Cf. *Ibid.*, 20–23, where he derives his information re Britain from Solinus. Dicuil follows Isidore in his account of the "Gorgodes," Fortunate Isles, and Hesperides. *Ibid.*, VII, 5.

[20] Modern commentators upon Erigena seem to have exaggerated his sources. Cf. Wright, *Geographical Lore of the Time of the Crusades*, 48: "In his *De divisione naturae*, beside the Latin sources which Isidore, Bede, and other encyclopedists had copied, he made use of the *De Nuptiis Philologiae et Mercurii* of Martianus Capella and also of various Greek works, including the *Geography* of Ptolemy."

See also George H. T. Kimble, *Geography in the Middle Ages* (London, 1838), 38–39: "His main work, *De Divisione Naturae*, . . . draws upon a wider field than was customary at that time. For instance it shows more than a passing acquaintance with the writings of Eratosthenes, Pliny, Ptolemy (he even speaks of his Geography), Capella, besides the usual patristic authorities such as Basil, Chrysostom, Ambrose, Jerome and Augustine."

Kimble fails to point out that Erigena's acquaintance with Eratosthenes was at best secondhand and both Kimble and Wright place more emphasis on Ptolemy than the passage they are basing their statements on seems to justify. Cf. *De Divisione Naturae*, III, 33: "Si autem quaeras, cur et Plinius secundus et *Ptolemaeus, in Geograhico suo, ut Martianus scribit*, non plus quam quingenta stadia singulis partibus distribuunt. . . ." The italics are this author's.

[21] John Scot Erigena, *Annotationes in Marcianum*, ed. and trans. Cora E. Lutz (Cambridge, Mass., 1939).

parently later modified his views and, in his commentary on Boethius' *Tractates*, rejected belief in the antipodes.[22]

Alfred the Great, whose concern for knowledge led him to sponsor the translation of many Latin works into Old English, felt that kingly prerogative gave him the right to add to or amend books he was translating. Alfred's alterations contribute to our study. His additions to Boethius' *Consolation of Philosophy* were of a general nature, and just tantalizing enough to make us wish he had added more.[23]

In several passages Alfred inserted familiar concepts, which, nonetheless, did not appear in the original, such as the view that sea water passed through veins in the earth, was purified thereby, and sprang forth to make its way again to the sea.

Even so from the sea the water makes its way into the earth, and there grows fresh; then it comes up at the spring, becomes a brook, then a river, then follows the course of the river until it comes again to the sea.[24]

. . . . . .

No brook is too small to seek the sea; afterwards it passeth from the sea into the earth, and so it goeth winding through the earth till it cometh again to the same spring from which it flowed at first and so again to the sea.[25]

This second statement, if Alfred meant it to be taken literally, contained a rather surprising innovation, in that the water after making its way to the sea was said to return to the *same fountain*.[26]

When he came to Boethius' allusion to Ultima Thule, Alfred

---

[22] See M. L. W. Laistner, *Thought and Letters in Western Europe, A.D. 500–900* (London, 1931), 146 n, citing E. K. Rand, "Johannes Scottus," in *Quellen und Untersuchen zur lateinischen Philologie des Mittelalters* (Munich, 1906).

[23] Alfred, *King Alfred's Version of the Consolation of Boethius*, XLI, trans. W. J. Sedgefield (Oxford, 1940), hereinafter cited as Alfred, *Boethius*.

[24] *Ibid.*, XXXIV. He has a less elaborate insertion similar to this earlier in the same chapter. Cf. Boethius, *Consolation of Philosophy*, III, prosa 10, trans, "I. T." and H. F. Stewart (New York, 1918).

[25] Alfred, *Boethius*, XXIV. Added to Boethius, *Consolation of Philosophy*, III, prosa 2.

[26] Conceivably the words of the Preacher in *Ecclesiastes* 1:7 could be

volunteered the following information: "That is to the northwest of this earth [actually 'this middle-earth'], where in summer there is no night, and in winter no day." [27]

Thus far we have been only slightly concerned with cartography, primarily because few maps from the early periods have survived and only a fraction of these have any bearing upon our problem. We have already acknowledged our debt to Cosmas both for the crude sketch by Ephorus which was preserved in his pages as well as for his own diagrams of the earth, which may be the earliest surviving Christian maps. We referred at the beginning of this chapter to the five circles within a circle diagrammed by Isidore which might qualify as a map of the crudest variety. This as well as Isidore's text had some influence on later works.

In one eighth-century manuscript there was a curiously twisted sketch which is commonly referred to as the "Albi" world map. Beazley, however, pointed out that in spite of its crudity this work of the time of Bede and Charles Martel was "venerable as the oldest geographical monument of Latin or western Europe in the Middle Ages." [28]

The lack of detail on the "Albi" map offers no hope of adding to our knowledge on specific points and one has the strong suspicion that the shape and extent of the ocean were dictated by the limitations of the page. It was, however, a beginning. One might note that the east was at the top, which was to remain generally true of maps until the introduction of the compass.

Beatus, a Spanish priest who lived during the latter half of the eighth century (d. 798), had a profound effect upon cartography. Although his original map, appearing in commentary on the *Book of Revelation*, has not survived, it served as the prototype of a whole family of later maps.[29]

---

interpreted to mean this: "All the rivers run into the sea, yet the sea is not full: unto the place from whence the rivers came, thither they return again."

[27] Alfred, *Boethius*, XXIX, 73. Cf. Boethius, *Consolation of Philosophy*, III, *metrum 5*.

[28] Beazley, *Dawn of Modern Geography*, I, 386.

[29] We shall assume traditional authorship, although it has been challenged, since that problem has no bearing upon our own. For a discussion of maps during this period see Beazley, *Dawn of Modern Geography*, I, 375–91; II, 549–63.

The oldest surviving derivative of the Beatus map is the "Ashburnham" map of the tenth century. This map depicted the earth as quite rectangular, but there is reason to believe that this shape conformed more to the conviction of the copyist than to the original, which was probably oval in form. The Beatus map is better represented by the "St. Sever" copy made in the middle of the next century. Other copies seem to be striving for compromise between oval and rectangular. Two are circular. It is quite possible that Beatus and some of the copyists actually conceived of the earth as a wheel-like orb, but practiced that curious type of medieval frugality which urged them to utilize as much of the page as possible at the expense of distorting the map. The "Turin" map could very well serve to illustrate Isidore's *Etymologiae*, which Beatus definitely used as a reference.[30] Here was the wheel-shaped earth surrounded by Ocean. The inhabited earth was divided into three continents and to the south, separated by the burning ocean from Africa, was the "fourth part of the earth" the home of the fabled antipodes. The Beatus maps lack detail. Therefore their worth to this particular investigation is confined to broad concepts such as those discussed above. All of the Beatus map derivatives accompanied commentaries on the *Book of Revelation*.

Bound with a tenth-century copy of Priscian's translation of the *Periegesis* there appeared a map without known family connections, although it apparently owed a great deal to some earlier one drawn to illustrate Orosius' *Seven Books of History Against the Pagans*. This is the "Cotton" or "Anglo-Saxon" map which has been reputed to be the "first map . . . to add to the knowledge of Ptolemy as regards Northwest Europe." [31] Crude though it was, it did show an attempt at detail not found in any contemporary production. It was produced in England and yet erred in some strange ways. Ireland was turned on its side, Scotland was twisted, and Thule was scarcely farther removed (northward) from Ireland than Ireland from England. Here too one feels that everything has been

[30] Although the Turin map and all the extant copies of the Beatus map, with the exception of the Ashburnham map, are later than 1000, it seems justified and perhaps wisest to discuss them here briefly as a group. This is also true of the T-O maps which are best exemplified by latter-day examples although the concept was widespread during this earlier period.

[31] R. V. Tooley, *Maps and Mapmakers* (London, 1952), 47.

distorted to compress the world within the confines of a square page.

There are many "zone maps" extant which date from these years (600–1000). These have as their purpose the diagrammatic representation of the five climatic zones explained in Cicero's *Dream of Scipio* and in Macrobius' commentary upon it. They are only maps in the broadest sense of the word and add nothing except confirmation to our earlier statements that such a concept was frequently a part of the medieval world-view.

Maps of another type with origins lost in antiquity were also popular during the period. These were the famous T-O maps. Although details vary somewhat, the concept involved in the production of these maps restricted the information they could impart. The initial letters of Orbis Terrae (the "wheel" of the earth) were thought to provide a key to the earth's physical appearance. If one drew an O and within it placed a T, the result was a map of the world. Above the T was Asia, to the right Africa, to the left Europe. The various parts of the T usually represented the Mediterranean, the Don, and the Nile. As time went on this system was further improved by lowering the top bar of the T until it coincided with the diameter of the circle or O. Then it was possible to locate Jerusalem at the very center of the earth.

Beazley noted that the conception of Jerusalem as the cartographical center of the earth did not "acquire definiteness and fixity till the Crusading Period. One of its very earliest instances is the Byzantine-Oxford T-O map of 1110." [32] He did point out, however, that the concept had appeared far earlier in written descriptions or allusions. Jerusalem, indeed, had biblical support for centricity, and equatorial lines had followed the axis of the Mediterranean Sea in the minds of Greeks and Romans.

None of the maps discussed in the preceding pages would have been of much help to the seafarer. In all probability, before the advent of the compass, oral rather than cartographical sailing directions were the rule. It is, of course, possible that some maps which did not survive, or have not as yet been uncovered, were more functional. Unfortunately, ships are more apt to sink than monasteries, and seamen are less apt to be archivists.

[32] Beazley, *Dawn of Modern Geography*, 556.

VIII *On the Threshold of Discovery*

K ING ALFRED, when translating Orosius' historical work, added a great deal to the geographical introduction concerning northern areas about which Alfred knew more than his guide.[1] He accepted the tripartite division of the orb of the earth which was surrounded by the ocean, reporting that the Anglo-Saxons called the ocean "Garsecg" or "spear man." His Thule, that "ytemeste land" called "Thila," was more specifically located than Orosius', being placed to the northwest of Ireland.[2]

Otherwise, Alfred offered no new information concerning Thule, a fact which could be of some negative, although not necessarily conclusive, pertinence. It does not corroborate the report that a sixth-century bishop, Kentigern of Glasgow, had sent missionaries to the Orkneys, Norway, and Iceland. It may also indicate a lack of knowledge of, or confidence in, the story of Sunnifa, who was reputed to have gone from Iceland to Norway in the fourth century to attempt the establishment of Christianity.[3] However, neither of these tales seems to have any historical justification.

[1] Kemp Malone has written two enlightening articles on this interpolation: "King Alfred's North, A Study in Mediaeval Geography," *Speculum*, V (1930), 139–67; and "On King Alfred's Geographical Treatise," *Speculum*, VIII (1933), 67–78.

[2] Alfred, *Alfred the Great's Translation of Orosius*, I, trans. B. Thorpe (London, 1902). *Orbem* becomes *ymbhwyrft; terrae* becomes *middangeardes. King Alfred's Orosius*, ed. Henry Sweet (London, 1883), gives the Old English text and the Latin original on opposite pages. The analogy of Garsecg as a name for the ocean to the trident-bearing Neptune poses an interesting problem but one beyond the scope of this study. For undersea mythology see De Latil and Rivoire, *Man and the Underwater World*, 23–31.

[3] Thorvald Thoroddsen, *Geschichte der Isländischen Geographie* (Leipzig, 1897), I, 13. He also includes other such references to Iceland. *Ibid.*, 13–14.

It has been commonly supposed that the names Greenland and Iceland appearing in a papal bull issued in 835 were also impertinent, the assumption being that these place names had been added after the period of Norse settlement and had not appeared in the original document.[4] These names, however, appeared as Cronland and Island in an early copy of a decree issued by Louis the Pious the previous year (834); the authenticity of both is supported by Farley Mowat, who cited a series of confirming papal bulls:

Additional evidence supporting the authenticity of the original bull of Gregory IV is to be found in the Life of St. Rembert, who was the second metropolitan of Hamburg, which See at one time held the administration of Greenland. St. Rembert's life was written by a contemporary of his about the end of the ninth century. In the first chapter of this biography is the statement: "Lewis, King of the Franks, established in the northern part of the Saxon province an archepiscopal see from which the preaching of the word of God should extend to the neighboring nations of the Swedes, Danes, Norwegians, Funelanders, Greenlanders, Icelanders, Scritfinns and Slavonians.

. . . . . .

To declare this whole complex of sources to be spurious, or to have been tampered with, is surely stretching scholarly suspicion beyond reasonable limits. To allow such a blanket condemnation would provide a precedent whereby anyone could arbitrarily invalidate any ancient document which was at odds with his desired conclusion.

These documents not only indicate that Christian communities already existed in both Greenland and Iceland as early as A.D. 830. They also show that the NAMES of both islands antedate their "discovery" by the Norse and so must be presumed to have originated with the Celts or Picts. Thus we find that the predecessor of the Norse name of Groenland, or Greenland, was Cronland or Gronland, which is in accord with what Plutarch and other ancient writers tell us about Cronusland, and the Cronian Sea, as Greenland and the Greenland Sea were apparently known in Britain early in the Christian era.[5]

If the authenticity of these papal documents is assumed, Alfred's silence becomes stranger. He had an active interest in land and sea to the north. In fact, the longest interpolation in his translation of Orosius concerned two exploratory voyages. One told of Ohthere, who sailed round the north cape of Scandinavia and en-

---

[4] *Ibid.*, 14. See also Hennig, *Terrae Incognitae*, II, 281–82.
[5] Farley Mowat, *Westviking* (Boston, 1965), 402–403.

tered the White Sea; the other told of Wulfstan's voyage into the Baltic.[6] Both he based on firsthand reports.

Such voyages serve as reminders that whaling was extensively practiced and that exploration, individually initiated and motivated by curiosity, was being carried on. These two instances, however, were only recorded by chance because of personal contact with Alfred, and we may be justified in assuming that the reports and not the incidents were unique. At any rate, the Celtic and Germanic peoples of the north were not strangers to the sea, even if no sailor from Iceland came to King Alfred's court.

Seamen from the tideless Mediterranean, accustomed to its steady, predictable summer breezes, were distrustful and uneasy in the Atlantic. They felt that there one might at any time be begaled or becalmed; the fog filled them with foreboding. Shore swells and tides were a threat, the vast expanse of ocean beyond sight of land a terror.[7] On the other hand, the seamen on the Atlantic coast had long since adjusted to the ocean that they knew.

Mute evidence that even Stone Age man in western Europe ventured upon the sea are the flint fishhooks, too large for anything but deep-water fish, which have been found at various spots along the seaboard from Spain to Scandinavia.[8] Nor is there any doubt that Scandinavia, Britain, Ireland, and Spain were all brought within a common sphere by able and active Bronze Age navigators.[9] When the arena of history enlarged to include the Atlantic seaboard, the people there had long been adept seafarers. Caesar describes the seaworthy wooden ships of the Veneti as well adapted to sailing upon the Atlantic.[10] Similar vessels are yet to be found off the coast of Portugal; this may have been the type of craft used by the seamen and merchants of Tartessus.[11]

---

[6] Alfred, *Orosius*, I. This is translated by Benjamin Thorpe and appended to his translation of Pauli's *Life of Alfred the Great* (London 1902), 238–528. (Ohthere and Wulfstan, 249–57; Thule, 259.)

[7] Cary and Warmington, *The Ancient Explorers*, 29.

[8] Cf. A. W. Brögger and Haakon Shetelig, *Viking Ships, Their Ancestry and Evolution* (Los Angeles, 1953), 10.

[9] For an interesting note on this point, see A. R. Lewis, *The Northern Seas* (Princeton, 1958), 109 n.

[10] Caesar, *Gallic War*, XIII. See Taylor, *Haven-finding Art*, 65–66; Piggott, *Ancient Europe*, 249–50.

[11] T. C. Lethbridge, *Boats and Boatmen* (New York, 1952), 118.

Rivaling the wooden ships were seagoing coracles, made of cowhide stretched over a light willow frame. Avienus had testified that the inhabitants of some small islands off the coast of Brittany (Amorica) were commercially inclined and roamed the sea far and wide in small boats made "of hides sewn together." [12] Pliny also had reported that the Britons crossed the sea to an island six days' sail from Britain "in boats of osier, covered with sewed hides." [13]

In the Celtic fringe area, where smaller canvas descendants of these hide-covered crafts are still in service, the use of the skin-boat in navigation reached a peak in the sixth and seventh centuries. Much of the Irish interest in seafaring was due to the missionary fervor of the Christian Gael, to the monastic tendency to seek solitude on deserted islands (which earlier citations from Plutarch may indicate was a tendency of long standing), to a penchant on the part of secular authorities for sending offenders to sea, and to the religious counterpart of this latter custom, the penitential sea voyage.[14] Piracy, trade, and the search for adventure also provided incentives. There is literary evidence that the Celts in their skin-boats skimmed far and wide over the Atlantic during the sixth, seventh, and most of the eighth centuries—the last great age of the skinboat. The impetus to build wooden ships came from the south, and these were soon developed to a point where they took over. Archibald R. Lewis has aptly remarked that the ships of the Veneti were the "only seaworthy, ocean going wooden vessels in use in the Northeast Atlantic prior to Roman times." He attributed the introduction of better wooden ships to the Romans.[15]

The last great age of skinboat navigation can be somewhat explained as part of a more general Celtic revival coincident with the disintegration of the Roman Empire in the west. British, Pictish, and Irish mariners plied the seaways. "Coruña in Galicia,"

---

[12] These may be islands off the south coast of Brittany. In the following lines we are told that Ireland (Hierne) and Albion (Britain) are two days' sail away. Avienus, *Ora Maritima*, 90–112.

[13] Pliny, *Natural History*, IV, 16.

[14] William F. Thrall, "Clerical Sea Pilgrimages and the Imrama," *The Manly Anniversary Studies* (Chicago, 1923), 276–83.

[15] Lewis, *Northern Seas*, 109 n.

Lewis notes, "was in the fourth century known as Portus Britanniae and a special lighthouse seems to have been built there for British seamen sailing to this distant shore." It is certainly not surprising that Iceland should be within their range, even if Sunnifa or Kentigern's missionaries were not specifically involved. Such Celtic mariners may have been responsible for the Roman coins appearing in Iceland with increasing frequency.[16]

Another reason for the Celtic skinboat's position of eminence in northern seas during this period may have been that those northern peoples involved in the transition to wooden ships, such as the Scandinavians, initially constructed craft less seaworthy than the ones of hide. Wooden ships of more southern provenance, however, may also have been involved in the shipping of wine and other merchandise from the ports of western Gaul and the Iberian Peninsula.[17] Although in seaworthiness the skinboat (and its ilk, whether kayak, umiak, or tarred canvas coracle) was not inferior to any other craft revealed by history in its first four thousand years, wooden ships increased in use and in usefulness. We have Caesar's testimony as to the sea worth of the wooden ships of the Veneti; and the type of ship which Pytheas the Massilian probably used in his Atlantic voyage has been certified as more seaworthy than the best ship of Columbus.[18]

The coracle continued to be used by the Irish and their Scottish kin and neighbors. Although the tradition would decline, such craft would still be considered noteworthy by a ninth-century copyist of Solinus who reported that Ireland's inhabitants were

[16] *Ibid.*, 32. See Orosius, *Seven Books of History*, I, 2.

[17] Lewis, *Northern Seas*, 25–26, 109 n.

[18] Stefansson, *Ultima Thule*, 18:

Markham ["Pytheas, the Discoverer of Britain," *Geographical Journal*, June, 1893] says, "A large Massilian ship was a good sea-boat, and well able to make a voyage into the northern ocean. She would be from 150 to 170 feet long—the beam of a merchant ship being a quarter, and of a warship one-eighth the length—a depth of hold of 25 or 26 feet, and a draught of 10 to 12. Her tonnage would be 400 to 500, so that the ship of Pytheas was larger and more seaworthy than the crazy little *Santa Maria* with which, eighteen hundred years afterwards, Columbus discovered the New World."

accustomed to sail the sea in skinboats.[19] By the fourth and fifth centuries wooden ships of advanced types were in use by Saxons and Picts, and by A.D. 600 the prototype of the Viking ship had been evolved by Norwegian shipbuilders. During the eighth century the Scandinavians began an initially peaceful penetration of islands to the south and west.[20] The Viking thrust followed. Pictish shipping faded away, although it has been suggested that Picts rather than Irish may have been the contemporaries of the venerable Bede who informed the latter of Thule.[21]

Europeans were not alone on the North Atlantic; Mela and Pliny both cited a lost work of Cornelius Nepos to the effect that "certain Indians," their crafts caught in a storm, had been driven onto the German coast.[22] Similar incidents were recorded in the reign of Frederick Barbarossa and in the sixteenth century. All but the last instance were seized upon as proof that the northern ocean was navigable from Germany to India. Where else would "Indians" come from? [23] Admittedly, the two banks of the Atlantic valley have always proclaimed their existence to each other. These "Indians" were apparently rather spectacular messengers from the west bank, although the message they carried was long misunderstood.

Undoubtedly, some of these western visitors made the crossing in their own version of skinboats. For purposes of accidental discovery the skinboat had several peculiar advantages. It was difficult to sink, and, if flat-bottomed as the ordinary coracle, impossible to control in a high wind. Having less draft, it was also

---

[19] Solinus, *Collectanea Rerum Memorabilium*, ed. Theodor Mommsen, 218: "*de incolis Hiberniae*: navigant autem vimineis alveis, quos circumdant ambitione tergorum bubulorum. . . ."

[20] Lewis, *Northern Seas*, 32. Lewis devotes considerable space in this volume to the various types of vessel in successive periods in the Northern seas from 300 to 1100. *Ibid.*, 46–48, 106–107, 168–69, 240–43, 314–15, 454, 509.

[21] *Ibid.*, 142–43; Bede, *Commentary on the Fourth Book of Kings*, XX, 9, in *Series Latina*, XC, ed. J. P. Migne (Paris, 1862).

[22] Mela, *Chorographia*, III, 5; Pliny, *Natural History*, II, 67.

[23] For sources and discussion, see Hennig, *Terrae Incognitae*, I, 289, 292. For a discussion of Eskimos in modern times making the sea voyage in kayaks from Greenland to Scotland, see Ian Whitaker, "The Scottish Kayaks and the Finn-men," *Antiquity*, XXVIII (1954), 99–104.

capable of greater speed (even in the wrong direction) than a craft of heavier material. The problem of the skinboat navigator was not so much one of making discoveries, but of getting home.[24] To this could be added: (1) that at least some of the Irish vessels under sail had keels which would cut down on the leeward drift somewhat and make them that much more precise in navigation; and (2) that deliberate "drifting voyages" were extremely frequent in Irish record and tradition.

Most modern authorities agree that in the great age of Atlantic navigation, which preceded the Phoenician period by a thousand years, nearly all of the North Atlantic islands and the American coast were visited by late Stone Age or Bronze Age navigators from Europe.[25] Such a view would appear to be gaining proponents although it seems to be much more prevalent among archaeologists and explorers than among historians. The former certainly have probability on their side.[26]

In navigation, as in many other aspects of their daily lives, the insular Celts were the last to relinquish their Bronze Age culture. Furthermore, the transition from paganism to Christianity was relatively smooth and peaceful among them, and the lack of any deep-seated enmity between these factions allowed a cultural fusion and the more complete preservation of a Bronze Age pagan tradition within a Christian context.[27] Christian monks with ascetic impulses set out to sea as avidly as their pagan predecessors had.

The extensiveness of navigation upon the medieval Atlantic is nonetheless difficult to determine and impossible to prove. It is, at the least, no longer possible to insist that up to the thirteenth cen-

---

[24] Cf. Stefansson, *Ultima Thule*, 39.

[25] *Ibid.*, 32–33. See also Brögger and Shetelig, *Viking Ships*, 9–47.

[26] Vilhjalmur Stefansson, *Greenland* (New York, 1942), 27: "Perhaps it will be as congenial to the next generation as it has been uncongenial till recently to assume that there probably were a great many crossings of every ocean and a great many discoveries of nearly or quite every land before the earliest that can be found in those histories which depend solely on books, on monuments with written inscriptions, and on 'dependable traditions.'"

[27] St. Columba's defense of the bardic order would be a case in point. See W. Douglas Simpson, *The Historical Saint Columba* (London, 1963), 58–60.

tury sailors had only the Pole Star and their own wits to guide them, and that their boats were no bigger than barges and no more seaworthy. The Pole Star was only one of many heavenly aids to the navigator, and the ocean was not only formidable, but helpful.

Early sailors were well acquainted with many signposts of nature. The flight of a certain type of bird, for example, could show in which direction Ireland lay. Many a sea-wandering monk determined, by whether its beak was empty or full, whether the head or tail of a bird was pointing at his future hermitage. The Norse Floki was credited with locating Iceland in that way. He prepared himself by taking three "ravens" along. The first one flew back toward the Faroes; the second circled and, seeing no land, returned to the ship; the third sighted land ahead and flew toward it, and the Vikings based their course upon this.[28] Other Norse

[28] The fantastic amount of information which a knowledge of bird species and habits can impart is revealed by the tables of birds apt to be near land, far at sea, etc., included in Harold Gatty, *Raft Book* (New York, 1943), 35–38. Cf. Gatty, *Nature Is Your Guide* (New York, 1958), 36–37, 174–203. The following passage from Taylor, *Haven-finding Art*, 76–77, is of especial pertinence:

> It has been very plausibly suggested, however, that their guide was the annual migration of geese between Ireland (as well as other parts of Britain) and Iceland. These noisy and conspicuous birds, the brent-geese, white-geese, barnacle-geese and grey-lags, wintered in their tens of thousands in Northern Ireland, and in the Shannon estuary (which St. Brendan knew). They fly into their feeding grounds, coming in from the north, towards the end of September and during the month of October. But ten days or a fortnight after the spring equinox they begin to leave. A large flock rises, and one long skein after another disappears over the northern horizon. A week or so later another flock departs in the same way, honking as they fly, and in four or five weeks' time the marshes are deserted—all have disappeared. They are on their way to summer breeding places in Iceland and Greenland. Flying along a direct route at about 30 miles an hour they will reach Iceland within twenty-four hours. Those which continue on the same line of flight across Iceland and then across Denmark Strait can rest if they choose before this second sea-crossing. But it is barely two hundred miles, for at Angmagssalik the Greenland coast bends north-eastwards. Whatever fantastic stories about the birth of barnacle-geese from trees the stay-at-home writer might repeat, the actual sight of these goings and comings year after year was to sailors convincing evidence of a land

mariners reputedly found Iceland by probing the ocean with the lead.[29]

A knowledge of the types of fishes and sea animals and their distribution, an awareness of the distinctive colors of various oceanic currents,[30] sharp ears and an ability to "interpret" the wind,[31] sharp eyes and the ability to read nature's signs and signals,[32] all came to

---

lying to the north. And the greatest authority on geese, Commander Peter Scott, states that there is nothing impossible in the monks' setting course by the northward migration, and keeping it by watching successive skeins of birds pass overhead. If the wind failed they could ply their oars, as St. Brendan's companions did, and in a week or less Iceland would lie on the horizon. The migrations, besides, both to and fro, coincide with the beginning and ending of the sailing season.

Re Floki, see *Das Besiedlungsbuch* [*Landnamabok*], 2, in Baetke (ed.), *Thule* (Jena, 1928), XXIII, 63–64. See Taylor, *Haven-finding Art*, 77–78; Gatty, *Nature Is Your Guide*, 43–44.

[29] Nansen, *In Northern Mists*, I, 251.

[30] *Ibid.* Cf. Gatty, *Raft Book*, 63: "The waters of the world have their own distinctions. They are in constant motion and derive their properties from their origin and the conditions through which they pass. Thus a current stream from the Poles containing a large percentage of fresh water from the ice will be cold and green. . . . The boundary line between ocean streams is usually very clearly defined, as, for instance, between the Gulf stream and the Labrador Current." See pp. 70–71 for map showing direction of currents and winds in February and August. Cf. Gatty, *Nature Is Your Guide*, 169–73.

[31] The Maelduin voyagers "heard" the sound of waves breaking upon a shore, and there are many other noises which would indicate land in a certain direction. The wind might bring the odor of burning peat or the smell of ammonia from a sea bird roost. Even if the wind brought no indication of land, it might, as Gatty points out (*Raft Book*, 54), still be helpful: "On most of the oceans of the world the prevailing winds may be used as indications of directions. Although by no means constant, it is possible to tell from the character of the wind, that is, by the temperature, humidity, force and type of cloud accompanying it, the direction from which it has come." See also Gatty, *Nature Is Your Guide*, 164–68.

[32] Another guide to navigation in the north is the ice-blink, discussed by Collinder: ". . . when you don't see land you often see a yellowish-white gleam in the sky near the horizon. That is the so-called 'ice-blink,' the light which icefields throw into the sky. Even at a distance of 60 miles you can see their faint reflection in the sky and where the sky grows dark again, there beneath is open water for which to head. It is sometimes even possible to see an open passage of dark water between ice

the aid of the instrumentless navigator. The sun was a daily guide, and at night there were the stars.[33]

The compass was not common in western Europe until the twelfth century and estimates vary as to when it was first introduced. The Norse did have one instrument in common with the seamen of antiquity which could help them maintain an east-west course in the open sea. This was the *gnomon*, or round wooden disc with a perpendicular stick in the center (of which, Herodotus said, the Greeks learned from the Babylonians). The length of the stick's shadow at noon could be measured and marked and a

---

fields delineated in the sky." Per Collinder, *A History of Marine Navigation* (New York, 1955), 42. Collinder concludes that: "There is thus nothing really strange in the fact that Norsemen early accepted the invitation to make ocean voyages which was inherent in the poverty of their country and the wealth of the sea, their good supply of timber for shipbuilding, the rarity of summer storms, the good sight of land, the warnings of the ice-blink and the guidance afforded by the auks. . . ."

Clouds also can be used as an indication of land. Cumulus clouds in good weather are caused by the moisture in the soil. Gatty points out that: "It is characteristic of high islands or coastal land in many parts of the world to have fixed clouds or cloud crests around the summits. At long distances off, when the peaks are not visible, these *fixed clouds* may be seen and may be recognized by *moving clouds* passing them." Gatty, *Raft Book*, 53.

[33] See Taylor, *The Haven-finding Art*, 3–20. Gatty's discussion of the methods of celestial navigation used by the Polynesians, the navigators who most recently sailed the seas without benefit of compass, may be of interest (*Raft Book*, 94):

They viewed the stars as moving bands of light and knew all the stars of each band which passed over the islands they were interested in. Their method of navigation by these heavenly beacons was to sail towards the star which they knew was over their destination at that particular time. This was an amazingly simple system and required no instruments.

To clarify this, let us imagine the stars stationary for a moment. Each star in the heavens will be exactly overhead at some place on the surface of the earth. If we know at this moment what star is over the island of Hawaii, we have a shining beacon standing immediately above the island and which can be seen thousands of miles away. If we steer for this star, we actually follow the shortest possible course which is called by navigators "a great circle." In modern navigation, due to the fact that a compass course is not the shortest distance, an approximation has to be made.

We then realize that the Polynesian system was more perfect in principle than our modern methods.

reading taken at noon each day thereafter. For a due east or west course each day's shadow should be the same. If the shadow was too long at noon the course had varied to the north; if the shadow was too short, the sailors were too far to the south.[34]

There are also indications that Celtic and Norse seamen had other instruments the exact form and function of which we no longer know. One such instrument may have been a simple astrolabe. It has also been suggested that the "sun stones" alluded to in the Norse sagas were actually cordierite crystal which changes from yellow to dark blue when its molecular alignment is at right angles to the plane of polarized sunlight. With such an instrument the sun could be located whether obscured by clouds or below the horizon.[35]

The Celtic and Scandinavian seamen who plied the waters of the Atlantic in the early Middle Ages were not as lost at sea as some have imagined. They had many friends we have forgotten.[36]

[34] Collinder, *History of Marine Navigation*, 91–92.

[35] Mowat, *Westviking*, 352, 354–55. "Magical Stones of the Sun," *Time*, XC (July 14, 1967), 58.

[36] See also Taylor, *Haven-finding Art*, 65–85.

IX *By the Skin of Their Boats*

THERE is no contemporary account of St. Brendan (c. 484–578), an Irish monk with a penchant for sea travel whose exploits were remembered and embroidered by later generations not only in Ireland but wherever Irish missions were established on the continent. Existing allusions of Brendan date from the ninth century.[1] Although the fanciful nature of many of the Brendan episodes is apparent, they represent part of a great seafaring tradition. Vilhjalmur Stefansson, who knew the North Atlantic well, felt that island descriptions contained in the Brendan legend indicated that Irish seafarers (not necessarily Brendan, since the deeds of many men often accrue to the most famous name) visited the coasts of Iceland, Greenland, and Jan Mayen Island. Stefansson also felt strongly that much else that was factual could and should be separated from the imaginative elements of the Brendan narratives.[2]

The geographer William H. Babcock, equally convinced of a factual nucleus within the legends, thought that Brendan sailed far enough southward to visit the Canaries.[3] More recently Geoffrey Ashe has provided a series of imaginative and stimulating suggestions concerning the significance of the Brendan materials to the student of oceanic discovery. He has opined, for example, that these even reveal an awareness of the West Indies. His entire recon-

[1] See Ashe, *Land to the West,* 51–52.

[2] Vilhjalmur Stefansson, *Great Adventures and Explorations* (Rev. ed., New York, 1952), 31–35. See also Stefansson, *Greenland:* 46–47; Greenland, "column in the sea," 48–49; Iceland, "smiths' forges," 49–52; Jan Mayen, "mountain in the ocean," 52–53.

[3] William H. Babcock, *Early Norse Visits to North America* in *Smithsonian Miscellaneous Collections,* LIX, 19 (Washington, 1913), 13–15. See also William Babcock, *Legendary Islands of the Atlantic* (New York, 1922); and Babcock, "St. Brendan's Islands," *Geographical Review* (July, 1919).

struction of the geographical knowledge revealed in the *Navigatio Brendani* deserves a considered hearing.[4]

Whether Brendan himself was the great navigator which tradition held him to be is of little import to us. Perhaps his own voyages were of minor importance and modest scope until enriched by tradition with the deeds and daydreams of others.[5] Our primary concern is in determining what someone may have done, or what was thought possible. Many accounts of voyages attributed to less famous personages are, of course, equally useful.

The Brendan account appeared in two basic manuscript forms, the *Vita Brendani* and the *Navigatio Brendani*. The two texts varied considerably but influenced one another and were frequently conflated. Both extolled the fame of Brendan as a navigator.[6] One of Brendan's primary purposes was to reach the earthly Paradise from which Adam had been expelled. That many of the earlier Christian cosmographers had considered such an attempt blasphemous was no concern of his. His search for this land, traditionally represented in the east, in the extremes of the western ocean, would seem to indicate that in his view, and in that of his confreres, the earth was not flat.[7] In the *Navigatio Brendani*, Brendan and seven-

---

[4] Ashe, *Land to the West*, 141, 301–302.

[5] See Beazley, *Dawn of Modern Geography*, I, 238. Cf. Ashe, *Land to the West*, 141: "While the *Navigatio Sancti Brendani* is a romance—we must never lose sight of that—it turns out to be as many have felt it to be, a geographical text such as to excite curiosity. The chances are that the author had access to a map or the equivalent of a map, a good deal more comprehensive than anything else that has survived from this period."

[6] For a guide to Brendan texts and a discussion of the voyages, see J. F. Kenney, *Sources for the Early History of Ireland* (New York; 1929), I, 406–17, 487–89. See also Charles Plummer, *Vitae Sanctorum Hiberniae* (Oxford, 1910), I, 98–151; II, 270–94; Charles Plummer, "Some New Light on the Brendan Legend," *Zeitschrift für Celtische Philologie*, V (1905), 124–41. The latter is extremely helpful. See also *Navigatio Sancti Brendani Abbatis*, ed. Carl Selmer (South Bend, Ind., 1959); Ashe, *Land to the West*, 52, 73.

[7] Fergil or Virgil, Bishop of Salzburg, is frequently reported to have been accused of heresy because of a belief in the antipodes. His Irish background would be of significance here. The letter written in 748 by Pope Zacharias to St. Boniface (*Monumenta Germaniae Historica, Epistolae*, III, 356–61) upon which the claim is based is, however, not at all specific about Fergil's heresy. He may have been simply manifesting the Irish belief in the world of fairy folk.

teen companions were said to have reached the earthly Paradise in a skinboat. The *Vita Brendani*, on the other hand, reported that after sailing the western ocean for five years with ninety companions in three coracles he transferred sixty of his followers to a boat of wood and with these found Paradise, not because of any superior seaworthiness of the wooden craft but because he had been told that he might not reach Paradise borne on the skins of dead animals. In a variant version of the *Vita Brendani*, Brendan's quest was not for Paradise but merely for a place of retirement, a deserted island in the ocean.[8]

In most of the Brendan accounts, the saint also visited a remarkable island, Insula Uvarum, which abounded in grapes. This has led some people, notably Fridtjof Nansen, to believe that the later reported discovery of Wineland the Good by the Vikings was merely a borrowing from Celtic fable. Others, however, have assumed the Irish borrowed their details from Norse sagas.[9]

In their wanderings, Brendan and his crew returned each year to celebrate Christmas with the monastic family of Ailbe who were awaiting Doomsday on an Atlantic island. There was once a considerable tradition of seafaring centering around this monk, most

---

[8] Plummer, *Vitae Sanctorum Hiberniae*, I, cxxii; Plummer, "Some New Light on the Brendan Legend," 125.

[9] *Vita Prima Sancti Brendani*, LIII, in Plummer, *Vitae Sanctorum Hiberniae*. Theories and hypotheses regarding the Brendan narrative are rampant, varied, and usually contradictory. According to Beazley, *Dawn of Modern Geography*, I, 235: "The voyage of the Moslem Wanderers (or Maghurins) of Lisbon, as recorded by Edrisi, and those of Sinbad the Sailor, as preserved in the 'Arabian Nights,' are clearly related in some way to the Brendan narrative." Thrall's essay on "Clerical Sea Pilgrimages and the *Imrama*," 283 says: "The purpose of this paper is to suggest some reasons for thinking it more probable that the pagan materials, Celtic or classical, are borrowed embellishments for voyage tales which sprang originally from the rich soil of religious legend in Ireland, particularly the legendary accounts of adventurous sea pilgrimages made by sixth-century clerics."

A. C. L. Brown in "The Wonderful Flower that Came to St. Brendan," (another essay in *The Manly Anniversary Studies*, p. 298) writes: "It is now generally understood that this *Navigatio Sancti Brendani* is little more than an Irish imram retold by a monk, who has Christianized the story as much as possible, and connected as many of the marvels as he could with biblical and legendary material."

of which has been lost.[10] In the *Vita Sancti Albei* it was written that Ailbe wished to flee from the company of men and seek solitude on the island of Thule.[11] In the same book there was a reference to a voyage made by Ailbe in an obviously supernatural ship from which he returned carrying a piece of vine with fruit thereon.[12] This might have been intended to indicate that he had visited Paradise, the island in the east which the Irish persisted in sailing westward to find.

In an Irish *Life of Saint Columba* there was another indication that East and West were thought to be in oceanic contact. It was reported that seven Indians, "children of the king of India," having heard of Saint Columba, sailed over the sea to find him. Although they died of weariness of the sea, Columba revived them long enough to administer Baptism.[13] Here also we might speculate as to fact behind fancy.

The Irish distinguished between two types of sea voyage in their traditional literature. One type was the *imram* or voluntary voyage; the other was the *longes* or involuntary voyage. (Both secular and ecclesiastical authorities used setting one adrift on the ocean as a punishment.[14]) In the *Voyage of Snedgus and Mac Riagla* are found both types. According to the tale, the Men of Ross have killed the king, and messengers are sent to St. Columba asking what punishment to inflict.

And Snedgus and Mac Riagla come from Colomb cille, having

10 Thrall, "Clerical Sea Pilgrimages," 281. Kenney, *Sources for the Early History of Ireland*, I, 409. Ailbe probably lived early in the sixth century. References to the family of Ailbe in Plummer's *Vita Prima Sancti Brendani* are in XXVIII, XXXI, XLI, LIV. For other sixth-century saints with whom sea voyages were connected, see Thrall, "Clerical Sea Pilgrimages," 282.

11 *Vita Sancti Albei*, XLI, in Plummer, *Vitae Sanctorum Hiberniae*: "Sanctus iam Albeus volens fugere homines, et videns se honorificatum esse apud homines omnes, et cum essent plurima loca sub eo, ad insulam Tile in occiano positam nauigare decreuit, ut ibi viueret Deo secrete solus."

12 *Ibid.*, XLVI: "Descenditque statim Albeus de naui, portans in manu palmitem cum fructu; et honorifice habebatur palmes ille apud Albeum tribus annis."

13 *Betha Coluimb Cille*, 113, ed. and trans. R. Henebry in *Zeitschrift für Celtische Philologie*, V (1905), 27–28.

14 Thrall, "Clerical Sea Pilgrimages," 277 n.

(this) counsel . . . , to cast sixty couples of the Men of Ross on the sea, and that God would pass His judgment upon them.

Small boats are given to them, and they are set upon the sea, and men go to watch them, so that they should not return.[15]

Much later the two monks, Snedgus and Mac Riagla, set out on a voluntary ocean pilgrimage and reach an island inhabited by Irishmen. These turn out to be the Men of Ross who expected to live on this island, along with Enoch and Elijah, until the day of judgment.[16] It would seem that God did not look with complete disfavor upon their regicide, since they too seem to have reached the earthly Paradise.

More famous is the *Imram Maelduin* which survives in an eleventh-century manuscript but was probably written down for the first time in the seventh or eighth century. In this story, Maelduin has decided to go to sea. After seeking out a Druid from whom to obtain a charm and a blessing, Maelduin and his companions set sail in their skinboat. Suddenly

. . . a great wind came upon them, so that they were driven (over the sea, all) that night until morning. And even after morning they saw nor earth nor land, and they knew not whither they were going. Then said Maelduin: "Leave the boat still, without rowing; and whithersoever it shall please God to bring it, bring."

. . . .

Three days and three nights were they, and they found neither land nor ground. Then on the morning of the third day they heard a sound from the northeast. "This is the voice of a wave against a shore," said Maelduin. Now when the day was bright they made towards land.[17]

Here we have a "drifting voyage" of which there are innumerable examples.

Maelduin also found a Wineland:

They were for a very long while afterwards driven about on the waves, till they found an island with trees upon it like willow or hazel. Thereon were marvellous fruits thereon, great berries. So of

[15] *Voyage of Snedgus and Mac Riagla*, VIII, IX, trans. Whitley Stokes, *Revue Celtique*, IX (1888), 14–25.

[16] *Ibid.*, XX–XXIII.

[17] *Voyage of Maelduin*, I–II, trans. Whitley Stokes, *Revue Celtique*, IX (1888), 447–95; (1889), 50–95.

these then they stript a little tree, and then they cast lots to see who should prove the fruit that had been on the tree. (The lot) fell to Maelduin. He squeezed some of the berries into a vessel and drank (the juice), and it cast him into a deep sleep from that hour to the same hour on the morrow. And they knew not whether he was alive or dead, with the red foam round his lips, till on the morrow he awoke.

(Then) he said to them: "Gather ye this fruit, for great is its excellence." So they gathered (it), and they mingled water with it, to moderate its power to intoxicate and send asleep. Then they gathered all there was of it, and even squeezing it, and filling (with its juice) all the vessels they had; and (then) they rowed away from that island.[18]

We have already seen that Maelduin and his crew recognized the sound of waves upon land from a distance. They also could determine their position and set their course by observing the flight of birds:

Then said one of them, seeing a large falcon[19] there. "The falcon is like the falcons of Ireland!" "That is true indeed," say some of the others. "Watch it," saith Maelduin, "and see how the bird will go from us." They saw that it flew from them to the south-east. So they rowed after the bird. . . .[20]

Another of the Irish tales was centered around the Hui Corra (Sons of Coira) brothers who undertook a penitential voyage to make amends for misspent youth. Although surviving in a twelfth-century manuscript, this tale also was based upon earlier material. It is revealing in several ways. In the first place curiosity as well as contrition is a motivating factor:

One day, when they came forth over the edge of the haven, they were contemplating the sun as he went past them westwards, and they marvelled much concerning his course. "And in what direction goes the sun," say they, "when he goes under the sea?" . . .

This is the resolve they formed: to bring to them a certain wright . . . to build for them a three skinned boat. The boat was built, so that it was ready, strong and staunch. This is the price

[18] *Voyage of Maelduin*, XXIX: ". . . they stript a little tree. . . ." Tree = *abaill*, accusative singular of *aball*, usually = apple tree; so this Wineland is also an "Avalon."

[19] *errach*. Stokes notes this is a word he has not met elsewhere; the type of bird is conjectural.

[20] *Voyage of Maelduin*, XXXIV.

that the wright asked for building it, that he himself should be allowed (to go) with them in the boat.[21]

The brothers went to sea with a crew of nine, among these a bishop, a priest, and a deacon. Before undertaking the voyage they took advantage of the good offices of the clergy and offered a fervent prayer—perhaps because of the number of novice navigators in the crew—for fair weather "and that the Lord would restrain the storms of the waves and the roaring of the sea, and the many awful monsters." Actually navigation would be no problem:

> Then they went on board their boat and began to row, and they were thinking whither they should go. "Whithersoever the wind shall take us," says the bishop. Thereafter they shipped their oars and offered themselves to God.[22]

A mighty wind drove them westward into the ocean where they found several amazing islands. One of these was a wonderful island with

> . . . a beautiful bright grove of fragrant apple trees therein. A very beautiful river (flowed) through the midst of the grove. Now when the wind would move the treetops of the grove sweeter was their song than any music. The Hui Corra ate somewhat of the apples and drank somewhat of the river of wine, so that they were straightway satisfied, and perceived not wound or disease in them.[23]

The *Voyage of Bran*, which also was of earlier vintage than the surviving manuscripts,[24] proclaimed that there were "thrice fifty

[21] *Voyage of the Hui Corra*, XXXII–XXXIII, trans. Whitley Stokes, *Revue Celtique*, XIV (1893), 22–69.

[22] *Voyage of the Hui Corra*, XL, XLII.

[23] *Voyage of the Hui Corra*, XLVII. There can be no textual connection, but the similarity between this and the island described by Euripides (*Hippolytus*, 742–54) at least a thousand years earlier is amazing: "Would that I might reach the apple-growing shore of the songful Hesperides, where the sealord of the blue ocean-lake grants to sailors no farther roads and attain the awesome boundary of the heavens which Atlas bears; where too are poured the [ambrosial] fountains of Zeus. . . ." This translation of the passage appears in Warmington, *Greek Geography*, 81.

[24] These are fourteenth- and fifteenth-century copies of an eleventh-century work, probably based on a seventh-century original.

distant isles in the ocean to the west of us," each of these being two or three times as large as Erin.[25]

Adamnan, the reverend abbot of Iona, wrote a biography of his predecessor, St. Columba, which tells us a great deal about the Celt and the sea. Moreover, this *Vita* is preserved in a manuscript which was written before 713. It contains over a dozen references to islands as monastic sites or refuges for anchorites.[26] Within these pages we also make the acquaintance of two other sixth-century navigators. The first of these, a certain Baitan, is only mentioned once: "At another time one Baitan . . . asked to be blessed by the Saint, when about to seek, with others, a desert island. . . . Baitan, after long wanderings over the stormy seas without finding a desert place, returned to his own land." [27]

The second seafarer was as unsuccessful but more persistent. Cormac Ua Liathain "not less than three times with much trouble sought a desert land in the ocean, but without finding one." [28] Failing in the first voyage because one of his crew was unworthy, Cormac tried again and plowed "*with full sails* through the boundless ocean" but "after some months" and "after long circuits" he put in at the Orcades. He tried again, and this time:

. . . his ship ran out from the land *under full sails* in a direct course, even to the region of the northern sky, the south wind blowing *for fourteen days and as many nights* of the summer season, such navigation seemed to be beyond the limit of human wandering, and return impossible. Whence it came to pass, that after the tenth hour of that same fourteenth day . . . certain foul and very dangerous creatures, which indeed up to that time had not been seen, swarmed around covering the sea; and with horrible violence struck bottom

[25] *Voyage of Bran*, 25, trans. Kuno Meyer (London, 1895). For the theory that Manannan, Son of Lir, who figures prominently in this and other tales, should be added to the list of Celtic navigators, see J. Vendryes, "Manannan Mac Lir," *Études Celtiques*, VI (1953–54), 241–54. Vendryes' thesis is that Mac Lir was orginally *mac lir*, "son of the sea," a locution for navigator.

[26] Adamnan, *Life of St. Columba*, I, 6, 20, 21, 33, 45; II, 18, 24, 26, 41; III, 5, 17, 18, 23, ed. and trans. J. T. Fowler (Oxford, 1894). For other references to seafaring, see I, 5, 18–19, 30, 41; II, 12, 22, 34, 45.

[27] *Ibid.*, I, 20. Cf. the blessing of the Druid in *Voyage of Maelduin*.

[28] Adamnan, *Life of St. Columba*, I, 6.

and sides, stern and prow, with such heavy blows, that it was thought they might go through the ship's *covering of hides. . . .*[29]

They also attacked the blades of the oars.

The wind fortunately changed from a south wind to one from the north (which Adamnan credited to St. Columba) and the coracle and crew made their way back to Iona and safety. Cormac, apparently, never found his desert island.

A century after Adamnan, in 825, a slender volume entitled *De Mensura Orbis Terrae* was written by another Irish monk and scholar, Dicuil. Dicuil, whose testimony on other topics has been taken earlier, also discussed the islands in the North Atlantic:

> In the sea west or north of Spain we do not read of any existing islands. Around our own Hibernian island there are islands but some are small and some are minute. Near the island of Britain there are many; some big; some small; some medium-sized. There are some in the sea to the south, others to the west, but they abound more in the region of the circle and in the north. *Upon some of these I have lived, others I have visited, yet others I have seen and of others I have read.*[30]

After citing the accounts of Thule in the pages of Pliny, Isidore, Priscian, and Solinus, Dicuil proceeded:

> Thirty years ago some monks, who had sojourned upon that island [Thule] from the Calends of February to the Calends of August, told

---

[29] *Ibid.*, II, 42. Italics are this author's.

[30] Dicuil, *De Mensura*, VII, 6. Translation and italics are this author's. Cf. T. C. Lethbridge, *Merlin's Island* (London, 1948), 91–92:

> One tends to forget that the monks had to store up food for the winter. This was clearly done to a large extent by snaring and drying birds in the breeding season. Perhaps this was one of the primary considerations of the choice of site for a monastic settlement. Bird cliffs near at hand, from which the winter's supply of dried puffins or fulmar petrels could be obtained, would have been of almost vital importance.
>
> . . . . . .
>
> The search for suitable bird cliffs would have led adventurous curragh men long distances over the ocean as they noted the direction of flight of homing birds. One thinks it strange, perhaps, that religious communities should pick on isolated islets for their meditations. It is not strange at all. They went there to be close to their food supply.

me that not only at the summer solstice but in the days around it, during the evening, the setting sun hides itself as if behind a small mound so that there is no darkness for even a little while, rather a man can do whatever he wishes, even pick lice from his robe, just as if the sun were shining; and that if they had been on the top of a mountain the sun would probably never have been hidden from them. In the middle of that short period it is midnight in the middle of the earth, and therefore I believe that, contrariwise, at the winter solstice and for a few days around it, dawn appears very briefly in Thule when it is noon in the middle of the earth. For that reason they are mistaken who have written that the sea surrounding Thule is frozen and that there is continual day without night from the vernal to the autumnal equinox, and, *vice versa*, from the autumnal to the vernal equinox continual night, since they [the monks], sailing during the time when naturally it is coldest, landed there and while remaining there always, except at the solstice, had alternate day and night; but they did find the frozen sea one day's sail from there toward the north.[31]

[31] Dicuil, *De Mensura* VII, 11–13. On the last statement, Stefansson (*Greenland*, 60) has this apt comment:

> Scholars . . . say it is suspicious to find our author quoting Pytheas about it being six days northward from the British Isles to Iceland, and finally to say, as if not quoting him but some priests who had been in Thule, the very same thing that Pytheas says about how far it is from Thule to the edge of the ice. These critics make two suggestions: that certainly Dicuil, and likely enough the priests, knew the Pytheas estimate; and that the priests did not *find* the ice a day's sail north of Iceland, as Dicuil makes them say they did, but merely believed it was there because they believed Pytheas.

> But what else than a day's sail (100 miles) could these wretched victims of the critics have reported? A hundred miles is what you and I would probably have to report if we tried it out; that is what the priests discovered if they did make the voyage. Is it not too much to demand that a traveler disagree with a previous traveler on a correct distance estimate just to show he is not a plagiarist?

A scribal addition to a manuscript copy of Solinus' book of marvels, apparently inserted before or during the ninth century, also concerned Thule:

> From the Caledonian Promontory it is two days' sail for those who voyage to Tyle. From thence begin the Ebudes islands, five in number. . . . The second station for the voyager is provided by the Orcades. But the Orcades lie seven days' and the same number of nights' sail from the Ebudes. They are three in number. They are uninhabited. They have no woods but are rough with reeds and grass, the rest is bare sandy beach and rocks. From the Orcades direct to Thule is five days' and nights' sail. But Thule is fertile and rich in late ripening fruits. The inhabitants there live from the beginning

Dicuil also included an account of the Faroes:

There are many other islands in the ocean north of Britain which, from the northern British Isles can be reached in a direct voyage of two days and two nights with full sail and steady favorable wind. A conscientious priest reported to me that after two summer days and an intervening night, sailing in a little boat with two pair of oars, he reached one of them. Some of these islands are small, almost all separated only by narrow channels. Upon them anchorites, sailing there from our Scotia, have lived for nearly a hundred years. However just as since the beginning of the world they had always been deserted, so now, because of the piracy of the Norse, they are emptied of anchorites. . . .[32]

---

of spring with their cattle and feed on herbs and milk; the fruits of the trees they keep for winter. They have women in common, regular marriage is not known among them.

This is Nansen's translation (*In Northern Mists*, I, 160–61). Nansen supposes the scribe to have been an Irishman and to have looked upon Ireland as the starting point. It is probable that the starting point would have been Ireland or somewhere on the western coast of Scotland. The seven-day sail between the Hebrides and the "Orcades" is either an error or the "Orcades" are not the present Orkneys. Nansen would substitute Shetlands but this, too, is difficult to accept. The Faroes are fewer in number, woodless, in the right direction, and much more likely to have been "uninhabited." The reference to marital customs is not convincing evidence that Thule refers to Norway rather than Iceland, although it does pose a problem which we will not here attempt to solve. The slower sailing speed may be explained in part by the increased use of wooden ships. Some 600 miles separate Scotland from Iceland and, although the maximum speed of a Viking ship has been estimated at around 170 statute miles in a day, a ship making such a voyage would more likely be the rounder, slower, safer type with little or no dependence upon rowers.

[32] Dicuil, *De Mensura*, VII, 14–15. Dicuil adds that these islands were still occupied by "innumerable sheep and an excessive number of various kinds of sea-birds." The Latin text follows:

Sunt aliae insulae multae in septentrionali Brittaniae oceano, quae a septentrionalibus Brittaniae insulis duorum dierum ac noctium recta navigatione plenis velis assiduo feliciter vento adiri queunt. aliquis presbyter religiosus mihi retulit quod in duobus aestivis diebus et una intercedente nocte navigans in duorum navicula transtrorum in unam illarum introivit. illae insulae sunt aliae parvulae. fere cunctae simul angustis distantes fretis, in quibus in centum ferme annis heremitae ex nostra Scottia navigantes habitaverunt. sed sicut a principio mundi desertae semper fuerunt, ita nunc causa latronum Nortmannorum vacuae anachoritis, plenae innumerabilibus ovibus

The Norse, because of whom the Celtic anchorites abandoned the Faroes, soon followed them to Thule, which was renamed Iceland. Again, according to Norse testimony, Irish monks fled before the newcomers.

The early Icelandic historian Ari (Frode) Thorgilsson (c. 1030) reported that when the Norse arrived in the ninth century there were Christians there whom the Northmen called *papar*; "but afterwards they went away since they would not live here with pagans, and they left Irish books, bells, and crooked staffs behind them by which one might tell that they were Irishmen." [33] Place names, some of them inland, also indicated an earlier Irish occupation, with their references to "papar" and "Westmen."

The Norse settlement of Iceland was rapid. In spite of its name it is not an inhospitable land. Winters, tempered by the Gulf Stream, are distinguished more by rain than by frost. Iceland has a capital city of about the same average January temperature as Milan, with no midwinter extremes as low as those of upstate New York. [34]

It has been estimated that by the year 900 there were at least twenty-five thousand people who called Ultima Thule home. [35] When the Icelandic Republic was founded in 930 there were fifty thousand colonists in Iceland. Well before 900, the prophecy of Seneca had come to pass and Thule was earth's end no more. [36] Around 870, land was reported to the west of Iceland, although the first recorded Norse settlement in Greenland was over a hundred years later. Shortly thereafter, the Norse discovered the American continent.

Did anyone precede the Norse to America? We have already in-

---

ac diversis generibus multis nimis marinarum avium. numquam eas insulas in libris auctorum memoratas invenimus.

[33] Ari (Frode) Thorgilsson, *Islendingabok*, I, in *Thule*, XXIII (1928) 41–57: "Demals lebten hier Christen, die die Nordmänner Papen nennen, aber sie fuhren nachher fort, weil sie mit Heiden hier nicht wohnen wollten. und liessen irische Bücher, Glocken und Krummstäbe zurück; daraus konnte man annehmen, das sie Iren waren."

[34] Stefansson, *Great Adventures and Explorations*, 43.

[35] Stefansson, *Greenland*, 65.

[36] ". . . nec sit terris ultima Thule." Seneca, *Medea*, 376–79, in *Tragedies*, trans. Frank J. Miller (New York, 1927).

dicated that we consider earlier visits likely. Were any of the
monkish mariners of Ireland among these visitors? [37] Here, too,
probability favors an affirmative response. The only recent champion of the Irish settlement in America who thought that he had
more than literary evidence on his side was the late William B.
Goodwin, an amateur archeologist, who maintained that he had
discovered ruins of ninth-century monastic settlement at several
places in New England with especially extensive ruins in Salem,
New Hampshire. Goodwin, however, was unable to discover any
artifact which would buttress his claim. His methods, despite his
gratifying enthusiasm, were frequently unscientific and may have
damaged somewhat both the site and the theory. [38]

The literary basis for Goodwin's claim, in addition to much of
the general material already touched upon, was supplied by references in Icelandic sagas to Norse meetings with Irish-speaking

[37] Paul Gaffarel in *Les Voyages de Saint-Brandan et des Papoe dans
l'Atlantique au Moyen Age* (Extrait du Bulletin de la Société de Géographie
de Rochefort, 1880–81), p. 23, concludes: "Donc l'Amérique a été décou-
verte et, en partie colonisée par des Irlandais, et, bien que le témoignage
des sagas manque de précision, l'existence de l'Irland it Mikla peut et
doit être considérée comme un fait historique."

[38] See Hugh Hencken, "The 'Irish Monastery' at North Salem, N. H.,"
New England Quarterly, XII (1939), 429–42; William B. Goodwin, *The
Truth About Leif Ericsson and the Greenland Voyages* (Boston, 1941),
161–65; William B. Goodwin, *The Ruins of Great Ireland in New England*
(Boston, 1946), 424; Ashe, *Land to the West*, 195-207; William G. Hen-
nessy, "North Salem Mystery," *New Hampshire Profiles* (August, 1952);
Evan Hill, "The North Salem Mystery," *Saturday Evening Post* (August
8, 1959), 32 ff.; Frank Glynn, "A New Prehistoric Settlement Pattern"
(Abstract of Paper, November 7, 1959; Eastern States Archaeological
Federation); Charles Hapgood, "Mystery at North Salem," *New Hampshire
Town Crier* (June 22, 1961), 3–4, 9; Charles M. Boland, *They All Dis-
covered America* (New York: Doubleday, 1961), 127–52; Andrew Rotho-
vius, "A Possible Megalithic Settlement Complex at North Salem, New
Hampshire," *The New York State Archaeological Association Bulletin*
(March, 1963), 2–10, 27; Andrew Rothovius, "The Strange Stone Struc-
tures of North Salem, New Hampshire," *Anthropological Journal of Cana-
da*, I, no. 3 (1963), 19–24; Robert and Osborne Stone, "Further Progress:
Excavation of A Strange Well at Mystery Hill, North Salem, N.H.," *The
New Hampshire Archaeologist* (December, 1963), 7–8.

For a novelist's view see Anya Seton's *Avalon*. For general discussions
of the Irish in America, see Hennig, *Terrae Incognitae*, II, 130–43; and
Ballesteros, *Historia de América*, III, 190–94.

peoples at various places on what is now the American coast, as well as references to Whiteman's Land, or Great Ireland, which is variously described as being "near" or "somewhat behind" Vinland.[39]

Norse settlement on Iceland assured the discovery of Greenland. Since the voyage to Iceland is the only difficult step on the way to the New World—one which E. G. R. Taylor has characterized as "dangerous and adventurous" but not "foolhardy" [40]—and since Irish monks were on this island, we can be quite sure that some Irish clergy made landfalls beyond it in their skinboats, perhaps even reached America. We have no evidence that they settled at Salem.

With the arrival of the marauding Norse vikings, however, toward the end of the eighth century, some of the wide-ranging Celts found themselves restricted to narrower compass.[41] The great age of Celtic navigation was over. The number of skinboats skimming the water at the will of God or seeking a desert in the sea rapidly dwindled.[42]

---

[39] All of the Goodwin sites are inland. The saga references can be found easily in either of the last two works cited above. For a disconcerting piece of the puzzle concerning Great Ireland supplied by the Arab geographer Idrisi, see Ashe, *Land to the West*, 152–53. Ashe cites the Idrisi text: "Between the extremity of Scotland and the extremity of Ireland, two days sailing are reckoned. . . . From the northern extremity of Scotland to Reslanda (Iceland), three days. From the extremity of Iceland to that of Ireland-the-Great, one day."

He feels that this statement, in spite of obvious errors in sailing time, supports the view that Great Ireland referred to Greenland rather than the American continental coast. This author, having elsewhere noted the mobility of Thule and Ginnungagap, is willing to concede the point—although the evidence is inconclusive—but must also acknowledge that the name might have been as mobile as the Irish monks were.

[40] Taylor, *Haven-finding Art*, 75.

[41] See G. J. Marcus, "Factors in Early Celtic Navigation," *Études Celtiques*, VI (1956), 325.

[42] If anyone has found the skinboat intriguing enough to want to test it in the fashion of Kon-Tiki, he can learn how to make one from Lethbridge, *Boats and Boatmen*, 119–20, 123. Lethbridge, *Herdsmen and Hermits*, 74, recommends a brief treatise by Jane Hornell, *British Coracles and Irish Curraghs* (London, 1938), which might prove helpful. See also Lethbridge, *Merlin's Island*, 78–118.

x *The Northern Way*

IN THE fifth century both the Irish and the Anglo-Saxons began to establish permanent settlements in Britain—the Celts to the north, the Germanic invaders to the south. The Anglo-Saxon invaders became, with the arrival of St. Augustine at the end of the sixth century, affiliated with Roman Christianity. The Germanic reaction to Christianity differed from the Celtic, and the fact that the Anglo-Saxon conversion was brought about by Roman rather than Celtic Catholicism increased the distinction.

The long sea voyages in search of solitude and other extremes of Celtic asceticism were not looked upon with approval by the Roman Church. The idea of "pilgrimage" became popular in Angle-land but the goal was usually Rome or the established shrine of some saint. After Celtic Christianity had made its peace with the Church, Rome and Europe in general became the goal of many Irish pilgrims. There was, however, an occasional surge of the old spirit. It was considered an event worth recording in the *Anglo-Saxon Chronicle* when in 891 three Scots came to King Alfred "in a boat without any oars from Ireland, whence they had stolen away because they would for love of God be in a state of pilgrimage—they recked not where." These three Irishmen had no startling discoveries to report to Alfred, but the chronicler did know a bit more about them:

The boat in which they came was made of two hides and a half; and they took with them provisions for seven nights, and then on the seventh night they came ashore in Cornwall and straightway fared to King Alfred. Thus they were named—Dubslane and MacBeth and Maelinnum.[1]

Although they may have disapproved of such "God-directed"

---

[1] *Anglo-Saxon Chronicle,* trans. E. E. C. Gomme (London, 1909), 67–68.

pilgrimages, the Anglo-Saxons themselves were possessed of a sea-faring tradition. The Old English poem *The Sea-Farer* has frequently been cited as exemplifying a Germanic enthusiasm for the sea:[2]

. . . my thoughts are now roaming beyond the confines of my breast; with the ocean flood my spirit roams widely over the surface of the earth, over the whale's domain, and comes back to me eager and hungry; in its solitary flight it calls urgently, irresistably impels my heart on the whale's path across the expanse of the sea. . . .[3]

It has been suggested that this poem belongs to the tradition of the Christian pilgrimage, and this thesis has been extended to include *The Wanderer* and the *Penitent's Prayer*.[4]

The foremost Germanic seafarers, however, were the yet unchristianized Scandinavians. The Viking ships for piracy and war were long and swift and the Vikings were not averse to traveling long distances on these ventures. Their raids upon Ireland and the northern islands soon turned the Celtic clerical seafarer away from the sea. Before long, however, Norse kingdoms such as those of Dublin and Man were to become centers of piracy and later of overseas trade. Irish seafaring traditions blended with those of the Norse.

Parts of Britain fell subject to the Danes and their fellows. Alfred opposed them valiantly and with considerable success—although less by good measure than most textbooks say—and, in doing so, brought about an innovation that whispered of the future. Alfred was responsible for a new type of vessel designed

---

[2] Cf. J. W. Bright, *Anglo-Saxon Reader* (New York, 1947), cvi: "This poem is notable as an early expression of the Germanic enthusiam for the sea, for storms and icy cold; even the thought that the landsman doesn't know what sea-farers must endure whets the sailor's desire to set out on the whale-road. Here is a new temper in the literature of the world; no such enthusiasm for bitter physical experience can be found in classical writings."

[3] *The Sea-farer*, 58–64, trans. Dorothy Whitelock, in her essay "The Interpretation of *The Seafarer*," in *Early Cultures of Northwest Europe* London, (1950), 266.

[4] E. G. Stanley, "Old English Poetic Diction and the Interpretation of the *Wanderer, The Seafarer,* and the *Penitent's Prayer*," *Anglica*, LXXIII (1956), 413.

for sea warfare with which he hoped to keep the Vikings from landing. His "navy" was kept up, and ordered out each year for maneuvers. In spite of some later periods when the fleet was neglected, Alfred may justly be called the "Father of the English navy." The ships which Alfred designed were large (thirty oars to a side) and stood higher in the water than the ships of the marauding Vikings.[5] In the field of naval defense, as in much else, Alfred had an illustrious predecessor in Charlemagne, who had reacted to the Viking threat by establishing a defensive fleet about A.D. 800. Charlemagne's son, Louis the Pious, expanded the Frankish naval defense system.[6]

The Viking "long ship" was short on safety in a heavy sea and limited in its functions and capacity. Just as the ship which Alfred built to combat it, the "long ship" was designed for a specific purpose. The Scandinavians had another type of craft which was broad and heavy, slower but safer, and much more utilitarian. The "round ship", or *knorr*, was used for carrying cargo and passengers, and for voyaging where the "long ship" dare not go. It was the kind of vessel in which generations of Norwegian fishermen, whalers, and sealers had acquired their knowledge of the sea. It was the type of ship which Ohthere used in his voyage northward, and the type which brought the colonists to Iceland.[7] It depended primarily upon sail. There are indications that its sailors knew the art of sailing into the wind, which they may have learned from the Celts, but they, just as the Mediterranean sailors of antiquity, seldom found this practical.[8]

From the beginning of the seventh century, the inhabitants of

[5] Brögger and Shetelig, *Viking Ships*, 178–79, 186 ff.; Lewis, *Northern Seas*, 262, 315.

[6] Lewis, *Northern Seas*, 238–39.

[7] Nansen, *In Northern Mists*, II, 155; Lewis, *Northern Seas*, 314.

[8] See T. Rice Holmes, "Could Ancient Ships Work to Windward?," *Classical Quarterly*, III (1909), 26–39; here the author examines the evidence found in the New Testament, Pliny, Caesar, and Isidore, and decides that working to windward and tacking were arts known to ancient seafarers, but that lack of a compass and other considerations made this impractical in the open sea. See also Lewis, *Northern Seas*, 316; Lethbridge, *Boats and Boatmen*, 152–66; Mowat, *Westviking*, 7; and P. H. Sawyer, *The Age of the Vikings* (New York, 1962), 74–75.

Scandinavia actively developed, or redeveloped, a deep-sea tradition. Remains of no ocean-going wooden ships have been found dating earlier. Deep-sea ships and seamanship developed rapidly in the eighth century. Ships like the Gokstad ship made the Viking raids of the ninth century possible. P. H. Sawyer has pointed out, in reference to the Viking ship: "The confidence of the Vikings can be more readily understood in the light of the technical perfection of their principle instrument." [9]

The Viking occupation of Ireland could not help but result in a fusion of the two seafaring traditions. It is frequently held that the Scandinavians learned of Iceland from Irish sources although, admittedly, accidental discovery was extremely likely. Irish monks were in residence on Iceland when the first Norse arrived and many of the first Scandinavian settlers were of Irish or mixed backgrounds. A. R. Lewis says flatly that: "The initial settlement of Iceland, then, can be fairly termed a joint Norse-Irish affair." He continues: "Probably Irish literature, like Irish traditions of seamanship and navigation, played a larger role in Norwegian civilization in the Western Atlantic than some historians have been willing to admit." [10]

For the Norse, as for the Irish earlier, Iceland, which has been characterized as "a cyclopean fistful of volcanic slag thrust up out of the North Atlantic," [11] could function as a stepping stone to the west. About 877 the east coast of Greenland was within the geographic horizons of the Norse. In 985, settlement of Greenland began under the leadership of Eric Thorvaldsson, known to

[9] Mowat, *Westviking*, 8; Sawyer, *The Age of the Vikings*, 75–76. The earliest sailing ship thus far discovered is the Askekaar boat. Two famous examples of ninth-century Viking ships, the Oseberg and Gokstad ships, were uncovered in excavations along Oslo fjord, the Gokstad being the more functional and probably more typical of the two. More recently five knorrs (*knerrir*) dating from the eleventh century, have been raised from Denmark's Roskilde Fjord. Cf. Eric Oxenstierna, *The Norsemen*, trans. C. Hutter (New York, 1965), 187–88. Cf. also Oxenstierna, "The Vikings," *Scientific American*, CCXVI (May, 1967), 66–78; Olaf Olsen, "The Viking Ships from Roskilde Fjord," *American Scandinavian Review*, LII (1964), 24–36.

[10] Lewis, *Northern Seas*, 267–70.

[11] Ted Olson, "Implausible Island," *Saturday Review*, XLVIII (September 11, 1965), 54.

his contemporaries and to posterity as Eric the Red. He had already explored the region during a three-year banishment from Iceland and, undoubtedly, already knew of land west of Greenland, having possibly visited Baffin Island during his first summer in exile.[12] It is Mowat's contention that the term Greenland applied not only to the island but to the territory across the strait.[13] He also argues, accepting the authenticity of earlier references to Cronland or Gronland, that Eric did not coin the name Greenland at all, and probably knew the name before he sailed westward the first time to go exploring or aviking (depending upon which opportunity presented itself).

Some of those who accompanied Eric in 985 were driven back by an angry ocean; others were lost at sea or came to land elsewhere—their fate is unknown.[14] Eric and the remainder of his followers established the first permanent Norse settlement in Greenland.

Eric may have hoped to find Irish monastic communities to plunder on his first westward venture. If so, his Viking luck was bad. There is, however, some indication that his settlers occupied territory that Celtic peoples had occupied earlier.[15]

The Norse settlement in Greenland would prosper. Christianity would be established there within a generation, in spite of Eric's objections. The Greenlanders eventually numbered from three to ten thousand, largely in two settlements which contained at least 300 farms, 16 churches, an Augustinian monastery, and a Benedictine nunnery.[16] The ever increasing number of hunters and resi-

---

[12] This is Mowat's premise, one which appears extremely plausible. See Mowat, *Westviking*, 62–66, 330, 343. He holds that the term Vestri (western) Obygdir (wilderness) refers to territory across Davis Strait.

[13] *Ibid.*, 398. As one who has been criticized for applying the term Viking to Eric, this author cannot resist the temptation to cite Mowat (p. 38) on that point. Eric "was a Viking setting out on a Viking voyage—with all that this implies. Moreover, he knew where he was going."

[14] They may have been caught in the *hafgerdingar* or ocean-whirl, a recurring phenomenon in the area which was possibly caused by submarine volcanic activity.

[15] Cf. Ashe, *Land to the West*, 152–53; Mowat, *Westviking*, 48–54.

[16] Michael Wolfe, "Norse Archeology in Greenland since World War Two," *American Scandinavian Review*, XLIX (1961), 380–92; T. J. Oleson, *The Norsemen in America* (Ottawa, 1963), 6–8; T. J. Oleson,

dents outside the main areas of settlement add to the difficulties of estimating population.

Before the Norse settlements were well underway, however, attempts were being made to push Norse frontiers even farther to the west. The continental coast of North America would be discovered and an attempt made to colonize this New World.[17]

Early Voyages and Northern Approaches (London, 1964), 15–17; Helge Ingstad, *Land Under the Pole Star* (New York, 1966), 22–24; Stefansson, *Greenland*, 96–98; Gwyn Jones, *The Norse Atlantic Saga* (London, 1964), 48; Marion Steinmann, "Leif Ericsson and His Relatives," *Life*, LXIII (September 15, 1967), 53–64.

Leif Ericsson's role in the introduction of Christianity may not have been as direct as once thought. See Magnus Magnusson and Hermann Palsson, *The Vinland Sagas* (New York, 1966), 19, 33.

[17] I do not intend in this work to discuss at any length the famous Vinland voyages, the accounts of which are preserved in Icelandic sagas, nor to enter deeply into the multi-faceted discussion of Norse settlement in America. This material has been extensively dealt with elsewhere. J. P. Swanton, *Wineland Voyages*, Vol. CVII of *Smithsonian Miscellaneous Collections*, (Washington, D.C., 1947), 4, has said that this is "one of those investigations which enable men who pride themselves on their acumen to prove it by leaving the problems ostentatiously alone or by registering skepticism, the cheapest way there is to acquire a reputation for scientific ability." In view of this, I feel constrained to go on record as saying that I accept the voyages as historical and devoutly hope that many vestiges of the Norse in America will yet be recognized, authenticated, and accepted. Moreover, the Yale presentation of the "Vinland Map" is a reminder that further documentary evidence may come to light at any time. Although the final verdict is not yet in on either the Yale Vinland Map or the excavations of Helge Ingstad at L'Anse-aux-Meadows in Newfoundland, I shall continue to follow developments with interest. At the same time, I concur with Gwyn Jones ("The Vikings," *New York Review of Books*, April 6, 1967) that these "would provide welcome corroborative evidence, but the case in no way depends on them." In addition to those volumes cited frequently in the text, the reader might see also Oxenstierna, *The Norsemen*, 245–63; W. S. Wallace, "Literature Relating to Norse Voyages to America," *Canadian Historical Review*, XX (1939), 8–16; Halldór Hermannsson, *The Problem of Wineland*, Vol. XXV of *Islandica* (1936); Hermannsson, *The Vinland Sagas*, Vol. XXX of *Islandica* (1944); T. J. Oleson, "The Vikings in America: A Critical Bibliography," *Canadian Historical Review*, XXXVI (1955), 166–73; William Hovgaard, *The Voyages of the Norsemen to America* (New York, 1914); J. H. Parry, "The Vinland Story," *Perspectives in American History*, I (1967), 417–33; F. J. Pohl, "Leif Erikson's Campsite in Vinland," *American Scandinavian Review*, LIV (1966), 25–29; F. J. Pohl, *The Viking Explorers* (New York, 1966).

Whether Bjarni Herjolfsson or Leif Ericsson made the discovery or whether, as suggested by the Yale Vinland Map, they were companions is a point which, for our purposes, does not need to be resolved.[18] Traditions agree that Thorfinn Karlsefni was a prime mover in the first concerted attempt of the Norse to colonize North America. Discussion concerning the actual location of the saga place names, Vinland, Markland, and Helluland, continues unabated and without any overwhelming consensus.[19] Nansen's contention that the sagas were realistic novels based on a retelling of medieval and classical myths has made few converts.[20] Most scholars concur that Ingstad's excavations in Newfoundland represent a site occupied by Europeans, and the Norse are the most likely occupants. Carbon-14 dates ranging from ± A.D. 680 to ± 1060 and certain details of construction do not necessarily indicate Norse. There may also have been temporary occupation of the same site in later periods.[21] The Greenland Norse themselves seem to have maintained at least sporadic contact with the Vinland area, wherever it was, during the succeeding centuries. There is some indication of this in the Eyrbyggja saga accounts of Bjorn Asbrandsson and Gudleif Gudlaugsson,[22] and in the statement

[18] Cf. Mowat, *Westviking*, 114 (note to second printing); Parry, "The Vinland Story," 421.

[19] See Hovgaard, *Voyages of the Norsemen*, 221–27; Jones, *The Norse Atlantic Saga*, 81–82; Mowat, *Westviking*, 405–38; Ingstad, *Land Under the Pole Star*, 147; Oleson, *The Norsemen in America*, 14–15; R. A. Skelton, Thomas Marston, and George Painter, *Vinland Map and Tartar Relation* (New Haven, Conn., 1965), 218–22.

[20] Cf. Hovgaard, *Voyages of the Norsemen*, 120–28. But see J. H. & L. L. Hill, "L'allégorie chrétienne dans les récits relatifs au Wineland," *Le Moyen Age*, LXVI (1960), 65–83: "La narration qui apporte le message moral ne doit pas nécessairement relater un voyage authentique, puisque la distance est dans le coeur et que l'expérience est l'expérience de l'âme."

[21] At this writing, Ingstad's scientific report is not yet available; but see Helge Ingstad, "Vinland Ruins Prove Vikings Found The New World," *National Geographic*, XXVI (1964), 708–34. See also Mowat, *Westviking*, 450–57; Jones, "The Vikings," 32–35; Parry, "The Vinland Story," 422–24; Magnusson and Palsson, *The Vinland Sagas*, 8–10; Hans W. Ahlman, "Rediscovering Vinland," *Atlas* (March, 1966), 187–90.

[22] Cf. Mowat, *Westviking*, 296–97.

recorded in the Icelandic Annals that Eric, bishop of Greenland, sailed for Vinland in 1121.[23]

Adam of Bremen, writing in the latter half of the eleventh century (c. 1070), was among the first scholars to incorporate the news of Norse discovery and settlement in the West in his writings. The fourth book of his *Gesta Pontificum Hammaburgensis Ecclesiae* was entitled "Descriptio insularum Aquilonis." Adam's sources included not only the Bible, Cicero, Orosius, Capella, Solinus, Macrobius, Bede, Paul the Deacon, Raban Maur, and probably Isidore, but also the archives of the archbishopric and oral reports from the Danish court.[24]

Adam of Bremen held that the earth was spherical. He explained that, because of the roundness of the orb of the earth, the sun in bringing light to one place left another in darkness.

He wrote that the ocean which the Romans called Brittanic was of immense size and "flowed endlessly around the orb of the earth, having Ireland on the left . . . , on the right the cliffs of Norway, and further off the islands of Iceland and Greenland. There the ocean, which is called dark, terminates." [25]

Adam began his discussion of Thule by citing Orosius and Bede (who had cited Solinus and Pliny). Thule, he said, was called Iceland, because of the ice which bound the sea around it. He then made the puzzling statement that the ice there was so old that it had become black and dry and would burn. Perhaps some member of the Danish court had used a lump of coal or surtarbrand to pull a cleric's leg. Adam further reported that Iceland was heavily populated and that the people depended upon animal husbandry, since grain would not grow there. Timber was scarce, so the Ice-

---

[23] See Hennig, *Terrae Incognitae*, II, 384–95.

[24] According to Beazley, *Dawn of Modern Geography*, II, 517, Adalbert, then archbishop, who was "practically a Patriarch of the North . . . made Bremen an Arctic Rome and his court the greatest centre of Northern learning." Later scholars prefer to modify this statement somewhat.

[25] Adam of Bremen, *Gesta Pontificum Hammaburgensis Ecclesiae*, IV, 10, 37, ed. J. P. Migne (Paris, 1884). This and the following translations are the author's. Adam's work is also available in a translation by Francis J. Tschan: Adam of Bremen, *History of the Archbishops of Hamburg-Bremen* (New York, 1959).

landers were forced to live in underground caves with their cattle.[26]

Not the least of other islands in the ocean, he said, was Greenland which lay deeper in the ocean opposite the Riphean Mountains.[27] Greenland and Iceland were both five to seven days from
Norway. The people in Greenland were cerulean in color and lived
in a way similar to the Icelanders except that they were more cruel
and given to piracy.

The Danish king, Adam wrote, had mentioned another island,
called Vinland, "which had been ascertained *by many* in that ocean."
It was so named because vines which yielded the best wine grew
there of themselves. There also, according to "trustworthy information of the Danes," self-sown grain was to be found.[28] The
Danish king had said that Vinland was the last habitable land before a region of ice and mist. The statement, originating with
Pytheas, that the frozen sea was a day's sail beyond Thule was
cited, and then confirmation was proffered:

This was recently investigated by Harald the most enterprising prince
of the Norsemen, who investigated the width of the northern ocean
with his ships, and when the boundaries of the vanishing earth were
engulfed in mist before his face, he just barely, by turning aside from
his inquiry, managed to escape uninjured from the immense gulf of
the abyss.[29]

The Harald referred to in the passage above was presumably
Harald Hardrada. Nothing else is known of such an adventure,
but there is no one more likely than he to have attempted such
an investigation. Some accept the voyage as historical;[30] others are
more reluctant.[31] Some associate Harald's ocean-probing voyage

[26] Adam of Bremen, *Gesta Pontificum*, IV, 35.

[27] *Ibid.*, 36. This, plus the earlier statement that if Ireland were on the
left hand, Iceland and Greenland would be way to the right, indicates
that Adam placed Greenland to the northeast of Ireland.

[28] *Ibid.*, 38.

[29] *Ibid.*

[30] Beazley, *Dawn of Modern Geography*, II, 525, 548.

[31] Nansen, *In Northern Mists*, II, 153–55. Here again Hennig, in *Terrae
Incognitae*, II, 365–73, is the best guide to a discussion of the problem.
The textual study involved in the Tschan translation of Adam's history
seems to strengthen the case of the proponents.

with a Runic gravestone inscription discovered in 1817 in Ringerike, Norway, which has been interpreted as: "They came out
and over great stretches and lacked material to dry themselves on
and food, further toward Vinland and upon the ice in the uninhabited country.—Evil can take away luck so that one dies early." [32]

Three reasons for associating the tombstone of this unknown
young man with the Harald voyage are: the fact that the inscription concerns Vinland and, in the text cited above, Harald's
voyage is associated with Vinland; the date assigned to the inscription puts it in Harald's period; and Harald was born in, and
otherwise associated with, Ringerike. [33]

The account of the voyage undertaken by King Harald is followed in Adam's history by a report of another voyage, this one
in the direction of Greenland. According to Adam, the source
for the latter was Archbishop Adalbert himself. Although much
of the information pertaining to the voyage itself is suspect, it
does serve to show us Adam's views of tides and has many
familiar echoes. It seems that in the days of Adalbert's predecessor,
Alebrand, certain Frisian noblemen, having been informed that
one might sail due north from the river Weser and never find
land, joined together to "investigate this curious thing," and light-
heartedly cast off. Fortunately they did not have a compass or
they would soon have found themselves ashore in Denmark. As
it was, they sailed between Denmark and England, their course
being northeast. They sailed past the Orkneys and Iceland until
they suddenly found themselves in the misty darkness of the
frozen sea where they could barely see ahead. Thereafter they
were caught in what was probably the East Greenland Current. [34]
The terrified mariners thought that they were being drawn toward
the abyss. Some of their ships were wrecked or lost but the remaining sailors, rowing desperately, managed to escape. [35]

The story thus far is quite plausible. We may doubt that they

---

[32] Hennig, *Terrae Incognitae*, II, 366. See also his Plate VIII. Cf. Ingstad,
Land Under the Pole Star, 98–99, 121; Oleson, *Early Voyages*, 29.

[33] Hennig, *Terrae Incognitae*, II, 369–73.

[34] Tschan in his note to Adam's history, IV, 39, suggests that it may
have been the Eis, a whirlpool off the east coast of Greenland.

[35] Adam of Bremen, *Gesta Pontificum*, IV, 39.

came close to the abyss, but they were as sure that it did exist as we are that it does not. Adam, who was equally sure of its existence, took this opportunity to explain that the gulf of the abyss was said to suck up the sea and vomit it forth again, thus accounting for the tides. Elsewhere he would reveal his awareness of a lunar explanation of the tidal phenomenon but gave no indication of accepting it.[36]

The abyss did not finish the Frisian noblemen, nor did their escape from the abyss finish their story. Leaving the darkness and cold behind them, by which we presume that they sailed southward, they landed upon an island with high cliffs which was inhabited by people who at noontime hid themselves in caves but left gold and other treasures at the cave mouths. Laden with this found wealth, the Frisians returned to their ships and fled just as Cyclops appeared on shore. They returned to Bremen where they told the archbishop Alebrand everything just as it happened and made thanksgiving offerings to the holy Christ and his disciple Willehad for their safe return.[37]

Somewhere someone had ceased to tell the truth. There is no reason to believe that Adam would have falsified the account related to him by his archbishop. Nor, for that matter, is there reason to suspect the archbishop or his predecessor. The best and by far the most simple explanation is that the thanksgiving offerings consisted of part of the treasure with which the Frisians returned, and that their story was fabricated, at least in part, to veil the fact that somewhere along the way they had indulged in a bit of piracy.[38]

[36] *Ibid.*, IV, 39–40.

[37] *Ibid.*, IV, 40.

[38] For discussions of this problem from two different points of view see Hennig, *Terrae Incognitae*, II, 354–59:

> Nun war aber Erzbischof Alebrand, auf dessen Zeugnis sich unsere Erzählung stützt, unzweifelhaft eine Persönlichkeit von Format, der man zutrauen darf, dass sie nicht auf den ersten besten Schwindelbericht hereinfiel. Er wird nicht irgend welchen Renommisten und Aufschneidern die Ehre eines Empfangs gewährt haben. Wenn er die friesischen Abenteurer nach ihrer Rückkehr um Auskunft über ihre Erlebnisse ersuchte, so liegt hierin ein Beweis, dass sie eine seltene und ungewöhnliche Leistung vollbracht haben müssen.

This, from p. 357, ties in rather well with our explanation although

Adam's references to Vinland were exasperatingly brief and vague. Nor would greater detail and clarity be forthcoming in the works of other authors. A passage in the *Historia Ecclesiastica* of Ordericus Vitalis (1075–1143) might have reference to Vinland. Ordericus alluded to the Orcades, Finland, Iceland, and Greenland as being subject to the Norwegian king.[39] Beazley and others assume that Finland here is Vinland.[40] The confusion of Vinland and Finland, linguistically, would be quite understandable. Furthermore Finland and Finmark were frequently confused and the confusion of Finmark and Vinland, considering the geographic placement of Greenland and Vinland suggested by Adam, was almost inevitable.

The saga material which deals with Vinland in detail appears in manuscripts of considerably later vintage. There has been much discussion as to the worth of saga testimony and as to whether the first oral accounts, from which the written versions were derived, preceded or followed the report by Adam of Bremen.

Fridtjof Nansen was in the peculiar position of accepting the Norse voyages to America in general while doubting the validity of the saga sources. He thought that "Vinland the Good" was simply the Norse equivalent of the Fortunate Islands, and that the entire story was based upon manuscript tradition.[41] He suggested further,

---

this was not his intention. See Nansen, *In Northern Mists*, II, 147–55. I had thought that the explanation was my own but a footnote in Nansen (II, 148) reveals that this theory was advanced by J. G. Kohl in 1869. Tschan agrees; see note 145 to his translation of Adam, IV, 40.

[39] Ordericus Vitalis, *Historia Ecclesiasticae*, X, 6 (Paris, 1852): ". . . Orcades insulae et Finlanda, Islanda quoque et Grenlanda, ultra quam ad Septentrionem terra non reperitur, aliaeque plures usque in Gollandum regi Noricorum subjiciuntur, et de toto orbe divitiae navigio illuc advehuntur."

[40] Beazley, *Dawn of Modern Geography*, II, 547. Augustus le Prevost, the editor of the cited edition of the *Historia Ecclesiasticae* (p. 28), declares that Ordericus does not mean Finland but Finmark. Nansen holds that these last are frequently confused but in this case Finland represents a confusion with Vinland. Cf. Nansen, *In Northern Mists*, I, 382 n: "The names Finmark (the land of the Finns or Lapps) and Finland were often confused in the Middle Ages . . . and the latter again with Wineland."

[41] Nansen, *In Northern Mists*, I, 353, 380: "That Lief . . . the discoverer of the fortunate land, should have received the unusual surname of 'hinn Heppni' (the Lucky) is also striking."

because of the extensive intercourse which developed between the Norse and Irish, that the idea of Wineland or Vinland may have reached Adam and the saga-writers through Ireland. Between the two positions there is certainly room, and perhaps need, for compromise.[42]

[42] Cf. Hennig, *Terrae Incognitae* II, 327–34, who here and *passim* disputes many of Nansen's contentions vehemently. Cf. also Babcock, *Early Norse Visits to North America*, 57:

> Quite recently we have been invited to find a sufficient explanation of Adam's words in his credulity which resembled that of many other old writers, in the possibility that he might have read or heard of a statement by Isidore of Seville attributing wild grapes, *messis* (perhaps grain) and vegetables to the ridges of the Canaries; in the fact that some ancient Irish sea-stories mention grape islands—as well as apple islands and other delectable places—and that he might have heard of them, and in the etymological, mythical, and every way mysterious relation of the unusual verbal form which we translate Wineland the Good (perhaps more adequately the Blessed) to the Isles of the Blest, the Fortunate Isles, the Irish Isles of the Undying and the fairy isles and hills of Scandinavia. But as Adam of Bremen adds no word, magical or otherwise, to plain Wineland—nor, for that matter, is any word added by the saga—we need not linger over the final point.
>
> But is it not curious that Adam himself gives us no hint of these classical, Irish, and north European sources; that the next European visitors, Verrazano and Cartier, Strachey and Brereton, Champlain and Lescarbot, are equally reticent in this regard, and equally positive about the grapes; . . .

See also Hermannsson, *Problem of Wineland*, 55: "[Nansen] set out to prove that it was all a transformation of, and borrowings from the classical and medieval legends about the Isles of the Blessed, or Fortunate Isles. His long exposition of this is so far fetched and improbable that it has found few, if any, followers . . . Never the less he has not written in vain. Without intending it, he has in fact disposed of any further attempts to connect the story with those legends. . . ."

But see also Jean Young, "Some Icelandic Traditions showing traces of Irish Influence," *Étude Celtique*, II (1937), 118–26.

Nansen found support for his argument, that Adam added a scholastic touch to the Danish king's report of Vinland, in a lecture delivered by Sven Söderberg in 1898 and published posthumously in the "Sydsvenska Dagbladet Snallposten" for October 30, 1910. Nansen (*In Northern Mists*, II, 63) adds a summary of this lecture as a postscript to his own discussion of Wineland the Good, which contains the following extremely interesting suggestion:

Söderberg "looks upon the tales of the wine and everything con-

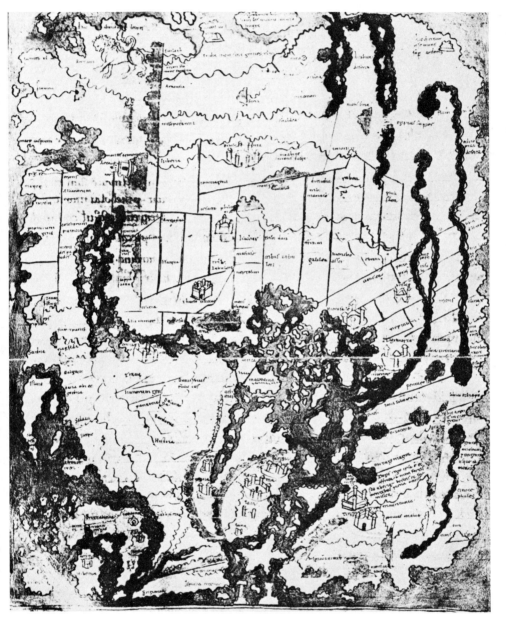

The Anglo-Saxon World Map

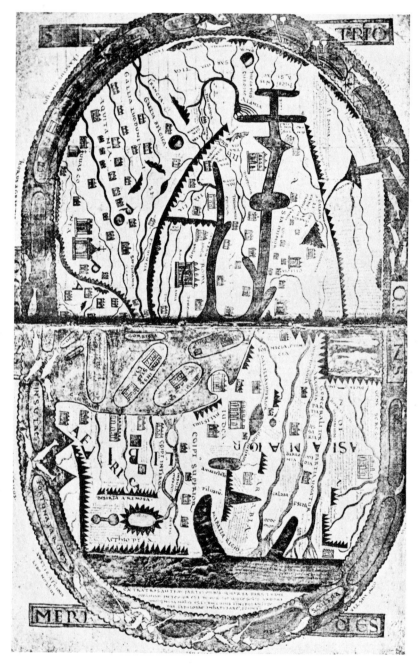

The St. Sever World Map

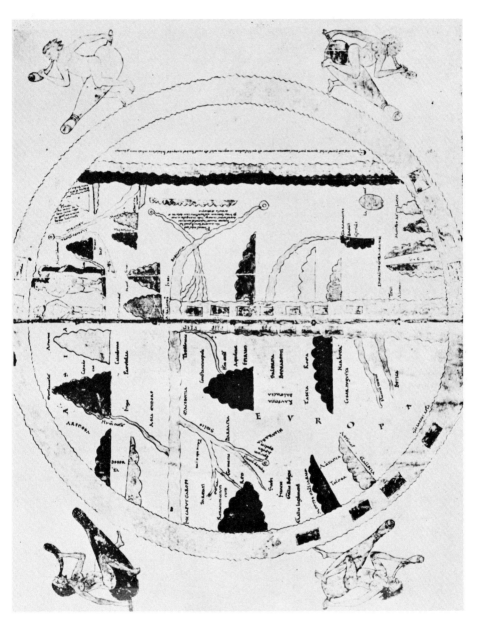

The Turin World Map

The Ashburnham World Map

An account of Iceland which may have preceded the report by Adam of Bremen appeared in *Meregarto*, an old German travelogue poem. This may be the source for Adam's information on "burning ice." The following section of the poem is pertinent:

There is a clotted sea in the western ocean.
When the strong wind drives ships upon that course,
Then the skilled seamen have no defence against it,
But they must go into the very bosom of the sea.
Alas! Alas!
They never come out again.
If God will not deliver them, they must rot there.

I was in Utrecht as a fugitive.
For we had two bishops, who did us much harm.
Since I could not remain at home, I lived my life in exile.
When I came to Utrecht, I found a goodman,
The very good Reginpreht, he delighted in doing all that
        was good.
He was a wise man, so that he pleased God,
A pious priest, of perfect goodness.
He told me truly, as many more there [also said],
He had sailed to Iceland—there he found much wealth—
With meal and with wine and with alder-wood.
This they buy for fires, for wood is dear with them.
There is an abundance of all that belongs to provisions and
        to sport [pleasure]
Except that there the sun does not shine—they lack that
        delight—
Thereby the ice there becomes so hard a crystal,
That they make a fire above it, till the crystal glows.

------

nected therewith as later inventions. He maintains that the name of 'Vinland' originally meant grass-land or pasture-land (from the old Norse word 'vin'=Pasture). . . . Söderberg's reasons for supposing that the word was still in use appear to have weight; and he also makes it probable that the name formed thereby might be Vinland and not Vinjarland. . . . Professor Söderberg then thinks that Adam of Bremen heard this name in Denmark, and, misinterpreting it. . . , himself invented the explanation. . . . [T]his kind of 'etymologising' was just in Adam's spirit. . . ."
But cf. Magnusson and Palsson, *The Vinland Sagas*, 58. Ingstad holds out for "pasture," Pohl for "vine," and Magnusson and Palsson for "wine." See also Hill and Hill, "L'allégorie chrétienne."

Therewith they cook their food, and warm their rooms.
There a bundle of alderwood is given [sold] for a penny.[43]

Very soon Icelanders themselves were contributing their writings
to the world of scholarship. The first, and one of the most noteworthy, of the Icelandic authors was Ari Thorgilsson (fl. 1100),
who has been called "the father of conscientious modern history." [44] Ari made a concerted effort to get his historical information as close to firsthand as possible. He wrote the *Islendingabok*
and at least initiated the first *Landnamabok*. In the *Islendingabok*,
Ari ascribes his information regarding the settlement of Greenland
to his uncle, Thorkel Gellisson, who learned of it from a companion of Eric the Red.[45] In the *Landnamabok*, the tradition of Ari
Marson, an Icelander who was driven by storms in 983 to Hvitra-
mannaland, was derived from a certain Rafn,[46] a descendant of
Ari Marson,[47] and corroborative testimony was given by the same
Thorkel Gellison.[48]

The attention paid by members of Ari Thorgilsson's family to
matters concerning the Far West adds interest to the fact that
Gellir Thorkelsson, father of Thorkel Gellisson and grandfather of
Ari, returning from a pilgrimage to Rome, was taken ill and remained some time in Denmark before his death there in 1073. It
was about this time that Adam of Bremen was writing of Vinland.[49]

As the Norse and Icelanders continued to extend their horizons
in the north and west, they were to evolve a concept of the world

[43] *Meregarto,* I, 37–83, in K. Müllenhoff and W. Scherer, *Denkmäler
Deutscher Poesie und Prosa* (Berlin, 1892), I, 94–96. For the dating of the
poem see *ibid.,* I, 196. This translation is from Nansen, *In Northern Mists,*
I, 181. Re present location of manuscript, see E. A. Ebbinghaus, "A Note
on the Meregarto," *Journal of English and German Philology,* LXIV
(1965), 232–33.

[44] Babcock, *Early Norse Visits,* 58.

[45] Ari Thorgilsson, *Islendingabok,* in *Islandica,* XX (1930) 51–52.

[46] *Landnamabok,* IX, in *Thule,* XXIII (1928), 95.

[47] Beazley, *Dawn of Modern Geography,* II, 72 n.

[48] *Landnamabok,* IX: "Dieser wurde auf See nach dem Weissmännerland
verschlagen, welches einige Gross-Irland nennen. Das liegt in Westmeere
nahe bie Vinland dem gutten. Es soll eine Fahrt von sechs tagen west-
wärts von Irland liegen."

[49] Nansen, *In Northern Mists,* I, 366 n.

and especially of the Atlantic Ocean which was peculiar to themselves and yet one which the learned among them were still able to fit into the traditional pattern. The lore of the northern navigators who visited or lived upon *Ultima Thule*, however, had little effect upon savants living farther to the south.

XI *Ring Around the Ocean*

℘OWARD the end of the eleventh century, Manegold of Lautenbach had a conversation with Wolfelm of Cologne. The two
discussed Macrobius' *Commentary*. Manegold was horrified to find
that Wolfelm believed that, in addition to the "known world,"
there were three other inhabited regions of the earth. Consequently,
he wrote a tract refuting Macrobius and Wolfelm. His position was
a clear-cut one. The inhabitants of such regions, if they existed,
would be cut off from the known world by vast oceans and an impassable equatorial barrier. Had not Christ come as a saviour to
all mankind? Surely, it was heresy to suggest that the inhabitants
of three quarters of the earth's surface were beyond the reach of
apostle and gospel.[1] Both thesis and refutation were familiar to the
medieval scholar even though, unknown to Manegold or to Wolfelm, the Norse and Icelandic voyagers had already succeeded in
crossing the impassable ocean in the north.

William of Conches (1080–1154) was born in Normandy and
educated at Chartres. He later taught at Chartres and, possibly, at
Paris. His most important work was *De Philosophia Mundi*, which
has been wrongly ascribed to several people, including Bede and
Honorius of Autun.[2] William agreed with the classical geographers

[1] Manegold of Lautenbach, *Opusculum contra Wolfelm Coloniensem*,
IV, ed. J. P. Migne (Paris, 1862).

[2] The text is included by Migne with the works of both these authors.
A later revision of this work (c. 1145) is called *Dragmaticon Philosophiae*.
According to Wright, this latter work, which I have not examined, retracts
some of the heretical doctrines expressed in the earlier treatise. Cf. Wright,
Geographical Lore, 398 n. But this seems to be disputed by M. Manitius,
Geschichte der Lateinischen Literatur des Mittelalters (Munich, 1931),
III, 215: "Darauf schrieb Wilhelm sein Dragmaticon wo er allerdings von
seinem Anschauungen keineswegs abstand sondern nur die Form des Dialogs
einfurte; wohl aber wollte er die Neuerungen des Ausdrucks und die
Gedanken, die sich mit der allgemeinen Kirche nicht vertrugen, zu-
rücknehmen."

and Aristotle as to the earth's sphericity and its division into five zones, of which the frigid and torrid zones were uninhabitable. He followed Bede in cautiously defining the southern temperate zone as habitable rather than inhabited.[3]

William thought that the equatorial zone contained the primary ocean which was source of all the earth's water and the ocean's salt. Two oceanic streams issued from this equatorial source: the one flowing east, the other west. Each stream bifurcated at the ends of the habitable earth, which resulted in a collision in the north and south. This not only caused the tides, but also set the planetary wind system into motion. William added that some thought tides were caused by the sea currents sloshing against submarine mountains and then flowing back. He gave short shrift to the Western Ocean which "is called Atlantic and in which is England and neighboring islands." [4]

Adelard of Bath was one of those western European scholars who in the latter part of the twelfth century was imbued with enthusiasm for Arabic scholarship, its methods, and the material it had preserved from antiquity. In addition to works translated from the Arabic, Adelard's writings included a treatise on the astrolabe (c. 1144).[5] His most famous work was *Quaestiones Naturales*, which purported to be a discussion between Adelard and a nephew. Early in this work Adelard complained to the nephew that discussion was difficult since the latter based his arguments upon authority while Adelard had been taught to depend on reason by his Arabic teachers.[6]

Adelard's view of the ocean did not differ materially from that of William of Conches. The sea became salt in the torrid zone, and this salinity was carried by the equatorial ocean currents to the remainder of the ocean. He had the bifurcated oceanic currents rushing to the north and south, but felt that in some way the

[3] William of Conches, *De Philosophia Mundi*, IV, 2–3, in *Series Latina*, CLXXII, ed. J. P. Migne (Paris, 1895).

[4] *Ibid.*, III, 14–15. The translation is this author's.

[5] His treatise may have constituted the introduction of this instrument to western scholars. The quadrant was introduced c. 1276. Cf. Kimble, *Geography in the Middle Ages*, 225.

[6] Adelard of Bath, *Quaestiones Naturales*, VI, ed. Martin Müller in *Beiträge zur Geschichte der Philosophie und Theologie des Mittelalters*, XXXI, Pt. 2 (1934), 1–92.

interposition of mountains and the rather elevated position of the earth itself prevented their violent collision. Adelard had blended the two tidal theories suggested by William of Conches, but his blend was less an explanation than either alone.[7]

Sometime in the latter part of the eleventh century, a very popular work, *De Imagine Mundi*, appeared, which probably was written by an English Benedictine monk, Honorius Solitarius[8] (although it has very often been ascribed to Honorius of Autun who lived during the first half of the next century).[9] This image of the world was Macrobian in some of its broader outlines but reflected primarily the geographical ideas of Isidore and Orosius.

The *De Imagine Mundi* began by placing the earth in proper perspective. The universe was round, but like an egg in that the earth was as a drop of grease in the center of the yolk. The ocean surrounded the land and also penetrated into the earth through subterranean passages similar to blood vessels in the body. The usual zonal division, three uninhabitable and two "habitable," was made, with three "inhabited" parts of the earth, Europe, Asia, and Africa, in the northern hemisphere.[10]

Among other islands in the Atlantic were the British islands and "Chile."[11] Here also were the Gorgades and the Hesperides. Here too was once the great island of which Plato wrote, which ex-

[7] *Ibid.*, LI–LVI.

[8] George Sarton, *Introduction to the History of Science*, II, 201 (Washington, D.C., 1927–31).

[9] *De Imagine Mundi* is found in Migne's *Series Latina*, CLXXII, among the collected works of Honorius of Autun. It also has been ascribed to St. Anselm.

[10] *De Imagine Mundi*, I, 5–7. The circumference of the earth is given as 180,000 stades, or 12,052 miles.

[11] *Ibid.*, I, 31: "Contra Hispaniam versus occasum sunt in Oceano hae insulae: Britannia, Anglia, Hibernia, Tanatos, cujus terra, quovis gentium portata, serpentes perimit. Isole in qua fit solstitium. Orcades triginta tres. Scotia, Chile cujus arbores nunquam folia deponunt, et in que sex mensibus, videlicet aestivis, est continuus dies, sex hibernis continua nox. Ultra hanc versus aquilonem, est mare congelatum, et frigus perpetuum."

"Chile" as a scribal error for "Thile" or Thule is understandable. It is intriguing, however, to see this North Atlantic island acquire the characteristics of Tylos in the Persian Gulf. See Cassidy, "The Voyage of an Island," 595–602.

ceeded Africa and Europe in size and yet sank with all its inhabitants beneath the sea which thereafter was curdled.[12]

There was yet another marvel:

> There is also in the Ocean an island which is called Perdita which by far exceeds all other lands in amenity and fertility in all things. It is unknown to men. It is sometimes found by accident but if sought for afterwards may not be found and therefore it is called Perdita. Here Brendan is said to have come.[13]

The tides were explained in *De Imagine Mundi* as the result of lunar influence in one chapter, and, in the next, just to be sure, as caused by a great whirlpool in the sea which sucks the water in and spews it out.[14]

A German geographer, Henry of Mayence (c. 1110) copied, interpolated, and added a map to the *De Imagine Mundi*. The map, however, which was a near relative of the later Hereford map, did not correspond to the text. Maps of this type preserved the quasi-circular shape of the "inhabited world," including islands by placing these in indentations in the shore line.[15]

Lambert of St. Omer (c. 1110) was a French cosmographer whose

---

[12] *De Imagine Mundi*, I, 36.

[13] *Ibid.*, I, 36: "Est quaedam Oceani insula dicta Perdita, amaenitate et fertilitate omnium rerum prae cunctis terris longe praestantissima, hominibus ignota. Quae aliquando casu inventa, postea quaesita non est inventa, et ideo dicitur Perdita. Ad hanc fertur Brandanus venisse."

One wonders if this was the island which Cormac was seeking. In an article by Maynard M. Miller, "Floating Islands," *Natural History*, LXV (1956), 233–39, 274–76, we are told that:

> The Sunkenland of Busse was sighted in 1578 off the coast of Greenland by one of Frobisher's returning vessels and possibly later seen by other explorers—but in a different place. People thought its position had been wrongly figured, but in later centuries no one could find it at all.
>
> In more recent times, there have been reports of Keenan Land, President's Land, Bradley Land, and Sannikov Land—not one of which could later be verified. Perhaps the most famous is Crocker Land, described by Peary in 1906 and duly noted on all maps. No trace of it could be found eight years later by Commander Donald B. MacMillan.

[14] *De Imagine Mundi*, I, 40–41.

[15] For a copy of the map, see Beazley, *Dawn of Modern Geography*, II, 564. For discussion see *ibid.*, 564–66. Re Greenland and Canadian Arctic on this map, see Oleson, *Early Voyages*, 96.

encyclopaedic work *Liber Floridus* was a bulky and poorly organized composition based for the most part on Macrobius, Isidore, Bede, and Capella. Lambert considered the earth to be spherical, and was convinced of the existence of antipodal continents.
His text was to be accompanied by a mappe-monde, but the oldest
surviving manuscript does not contain one although it has two
Macrobian zone sketches, a T-O design, and a map of the quarter
of the world containing Europe. The Europe map has one point of
interest: Thule is indicated as lying far to the south, off Gibraltar.[16] Later manuscripts contain a mappe-monde which is indubi-
tably a copy of Lambert's original. That Lambert considered the
Australian continent to be inhabited, although no one could cross
the equatorial sea, is indicated by the inscription on the mappe-
monde itself. Augustine's objections were met by making the antipodal population another genus.[17]

Lambert's map of the world stressed the antipodes more than
most. In addition to the southern continent, which occupied the entire bottom half, there was a circle to the east entitled "Paradise" which was balanced by one of the west labeled "Our Antipodes." Here, too, Thule was at the mouth of the Mediterranean.
South of it was an island of the Blessed (Beata) and below this
the Gorgades.[18] Beazley speculated that the Lambert map, with
the exception of a few more recent additions, had been taken from
an ancient world sketch of the fourth or fifth century.[19] It was
apparently left until more recently for someone to point out that
the inscription at the upper right side of the map attributes it to
Capella.[20] Whether Lambert or some much earlier copyist added
Paradise is undetermined.

[16] A copy of this map appears in Migne's *Series Latina*, CLXIII, cols.
1027–28. For Lambert of St. Omer, *Liber Floridus* (Notitia et Excerpta),
see *ibid.*, col. 1003–31. See also Beazley, *Dawn of Modern Geography*, II,
570–74, 621–24.

[17] Cf. Lambert, *Liber Floridus*, in *Series Latina*, CLXIII, ed. J. P. Migne
(Paris, 1893), col. 1009: "Zona australis temperata, habitabilis, sed incog-
nita hominibus nostri generis."

[18] There are other islands farther down the African coast, the names
of which I cannot make out; they may be the "Fortunate Isles."

[19] Beazley, *Dawn of Modern Geography*, II, 572–73, 624.

[20] Kimble, *Geography in the Middle Ages*, 9 n. Plate II in this work
is a reproduction of the Lambert Map. The inscription can be read, even
at this reduced scale, with the naked eye.

Peter Abelard (1079–1142) ventured into geographical waters long enough to offer an amazing compromise in his *Expositio in Hexaemeron*. His earth was a sphere which floated partially submerged in the ocean:

Just as any globe may be placed in water so that one part of it rises above the water, even so the globe of the earth rests in the waters so that the sea is in contact with one side of it and pours through its veins, whence springs and rivers take their rise.[21]

Geoffrey of Monmouth (d. 1154) in his monumental *History of the Kings of Britain* had two of the British kings subjugating Iceland—Arthur himself and Malgo.[22] This testimony is, to say the least, suspect; he was more helpful elsewhere. In his *Vita Merlini*, he inserted a geographical treatise. Herein the earth was divided into five zones; the two temperate zones were "inhabited." The sky embraced everything "like the shell surrounding a nut." The sea girded the land in four circles, and "with its mighty refluence" so struck the air as to generate the winds. The burning equatorial sea surrounded the Christian hell: "That part which burns surrounds a gulf and a fierce people. . . . Thither descend those who transgress the laws and reject God." The sea in the temperate zone was bountiful and good and bore "back and forth ships carrying our commerce, by the profits of which the poor man becomes suddenly rich." [23]

[21] Abelard, "Third day," *Expositio in Hexaemeron*, ed. J. P. Migne (Paris, 1879): "Quasi enim aliquis globus ita in aqua constituatur, ut una pars ejus superemineat, ita ille globus terrae in aquis insedit, ut ex una parte eum mare contingeret, et per venas ejus se infunderet, unde nobis fontes vel flumina nascerentur."

[22] Geoffrey of Monmouth, *Historia Regum Britanniae*, IX, 10; XI, 7, ed. A. Griscom (New York, 1929). Cf. Babcock, *Early Norse Visits*, 12:
The ancient poem in the Book of Taliesin [*Spoils of Annwn*] . . . seems to have a nucleus of reality, though surrounding the British leader . . . with the accessories borrowed from some fading pagan god. At any rate these verses may have been the germ of the fictitious Arthurian conquest of Ireland and Iceland related by Geoffrey of Monmouth . . . —who in this instance has found a believer to some extent in even the veteran investigator Rev. B. F. Costa, for the latter says ["Arctic Exploration" in *American Geographical Society Bulletin*, 1880, p. 163]: The expedition to Iceland may be regarded as historic.

[23] Geoffrey of Monmouth, *Vita Merlini*, ed. and trans. John Jay Perry, *University of Illinois Studies in Language and Literature*, X (August, 1925), 75–85, 744–46, 792–97, 813–14.

Geoffrey, putting words in the mouth of Taliesin, reported that there were many inhabited "realms among the waves," the foremost of which was Britain. Near this lay Thanet (Thanatos), "which abounds in many things but lacks the death dealing serpent"; Ireland, which was also snake-free; and the Orkneys.[24] The account of Thule was strange and book-learned:

> Thule [ytilie] receives its name "furthest" from the sun, because of the solstice which the summer sun makes there, turning its rays and shining no further, and taking away the day, so that always throughout the long night the air is full of shadows, and making a bridge congealed by the benumbing cold, which prevents the passage of ships.[25]

In a passage which directly equated the Fortunate Islands of the classical world with the Celtic Avalon, he described the "island of apples which men call 'The Fortunate Isle,'" which received its name "from the fact that it produces all things of itself; the fields there have no need of the ploughs of the farmers." There were grain, and grapes, and apple trees in abundance. Moreover, this was the home of the sorceress Morgan and to this island the wounded Arthur was taken.[26]

In the work of Hugo of St. Victor (d. 1141) the mystical approach to geography once again came to the fore. His geographical concepts were conditioned by a literal reading of the Bible. He explained the common source of all the earth's water was the "great abyss." [27] Many of his statements on the six days of creation have earlier counterparts. His system of map-making approached uniqueness, although it was reminiscent of Cosmas in method. Hugo was quite interested in the symbolism of Noah's ark, and he wrote two treatises upon it—*De Arca Noe Mystica* and *De Arca*

[24] *Ibid.*, 856.

[25] *Ibid.*, 881–86.

[26] *Ibid.*, 908: "Insula pomorum que fortunata uocatur." For Avalon and Arthurian Romance see Tom Peete Cross, "The Passing of Arthur," *The Manly Anniversary Studies*, 284–94. For Avalon as an antipodal land mass one might begin with William A. Nitze, "Erec and the Joy of the Court," *Speculum*, XXIX (1954), 700: "And the satirical Draco Normannicus, written about 1170, lets King Arthur—from his retreat in the Antipodes—write Henry II a letter. . . ."

[27] Hugo of St. Victor, *De Sacramentis*, I, 1, xxii, in *Series Latina*, CLXXVI, ed. J. P. Migne (Paris 1879).

Noe Morali. In the shape of the ark he found the clues from which he constructed his world picture. The ark being rectangular and longer than wide, he began with such a rectangle. Then he drew an oval around this rectangle touching it at each of the four corners. Within this oblong circle was the mappe-monde. The segment of the oval cut off by the front of the arc was Paradise. The segment to the west, cut off by the rear of the ark, was the universal resurrection. From there the elect would go to the southern segment (where Geoffrey had placed Hell), the damned to Hell in the north. Beyond this oval there was another circle upon which the zones were shown. Between the circles there was air.[28]

Hugo expected the Atlantic Ocean (the western segment of his world) soon to be the scene of considerable activity. The history of man had begun in the east with Adam, and the flow of civilization had since been westward. Hugo stood at the end of the world at the end of centuries prepared to make his spiritual passage with the rest of mankind across the Atlantic to the last judgment.[29]

Nikulas Saemundarson (d. 1158) was an Icelandic monk who made a pilgrimage to the Holy Land and thereafter wrote a geographical treatise into which he incorporated his itinerary. Nikulas considered Greenland to be a part of the mainland:

[28] Hugo of St. Victor, *De Arca Noe Mystica*, XIV, in *Series Latina*, CLXXVI, ed. J. P. Migne (Paris, 1879):

Hoc modo arca perfecta, circumdicitur et circulus oblongus, qui ad singula cornua eam contingat, et spatium quod circumferentia ejus includit, est orbis terrae. In hoc spatio mappa mundi depingitur ita ut caput arcae ad orientem convertatur, et finis ejus occidentem contingat, ut mirabili dispositione ab eodem principe decurrat situs locorum cum ordine temporum, et idem sit finis mundi, qui est finis saeculi. Conus autem ille circuli, qui in captite arcae prominet ad orientem, Paradisus est. . . . Cornus alter, qui prominet ad occidentem, habet universalis resurrectionis judicium in dextra electos, in sinistra reprobos. In cujus coni angulo Aquilonari est infernus, quo damnandi cum apostatis spiribus detrudentur. Post haec supradicto circulo alter paulo laxior circumducitur, ut quasi zonam videatur efficere, et hoc spatium aer est.

[29] Hugo of St. Victor, *De Arca Noe Morali*, IV, 9, in *Series Latina*, CLXXVI, ed. J. P. Migne (Paris, 1879): "Imo primus homo in Oriente, in hortis Eden jam conditus collacatur, ut ab illo principio propago posteritatis in orbem proflueret. Item post diluvium principium regnorum et caput mundi in Assyriis, et Chaldaeis, et Medis in partibus Orientis fuit. Deinde ad Graecos venit, postremo circa finem saeculi ad Romanos in Occidente, quasi in fine mundi habitantes, postestas summa descendit."

To the north of Norway is Finmark. From thence the land turns towards the north-east, and then to the east before one comes to Bjarmeland. . . . From Bjarmeland the land stretches to the uninhabited parts of the north, until Greenland begins.[30]

South of Greenland, according to Nikulas, was Helluland; next to it was Markland and then it was not far to Vinland the Good, "which some think to be connected with Africa." The Atlantic, having become a mediterranean sea, was also to have its Strait of Gibraltar; Nikulas or a scribal copyist added that if Vinland were connected with Africa, "then the outer ocean must fall in between Vinland and Markland." [31]

Although the Icelanders were among the foremost sailors of the period, there has been no evidence until recently that they made sketches or maps of the regions they visited and explored. Instead they relied primarily upon information and observation incorporated in an oral tradition, some of which was later written down. During the twelfth and thirteenth centuries, examples of conventional medieval cartography found their way to Iceland.[32] By that time, however, the Norse, and in particular the Icelanders, had developed some original concepts of their own.[33] Adam of Bre-

[30] There has been some debate whether Nikulas Saemundarson of Thingeyrar or Nikulas Bergsson of Thvera was the author of this work. I have gone along with Sarton, *Introduction to the History of Science*, II, 421. This passage is cited by Nansen, *In Northern Mists*, II, 237, from an "older ms." The variant version which is continued below, reads: "Nearest Denmark is lesser Sweden, there is Öland, then Gotland, then Helsingeland then Vermeland, then two Kvaenlands, and they are north of Bjarmeland. From Bjarmeland uninhabited country extends northward as far as Greenland. South of Greenland is Helluland."

[31] *Ibid.*, II, 1. Hennig, *Terrae Incognitae*, II, 317, cites this passage from Nikolaus von Thingeyrar, *Erdkundebuch*, in *Islezk Fornrit*, IV (Reykjavik, 1935). Hennig makes the point (*Ibid.*, II, 327) that the fact that Vinland was no longer considered an island indicates some idea of its extent.

[32] Halldór Hermannsson, *Two Icelandic Cartographers*, in *Islandica*, XVII (1926) 1. This was probably the stimulant for much of the developing saga literature and one of the arguments for giving at least limited credence to many of their details.

[33] See Vincent Cassidy, "The Location of Ginnunga-gap." *Scandinavian Studies, Essays Presented to Dr. Henry Goddard Leach on the Occasion of his 85th Birthday*, ed. Carl F. Bayerschmidt and Erik J. Friis (Seattle, 1965), 27–38; R. A. Skelton, *The European Image and Mapping of America*,

men's view of the northern ocean and its islands and coasts conformed to the traditional world picture. He adapted the new discoveries to it. Nikulas, on the other hand, tried to adapt the traditional world picture to the new discoveries. There were many
later scholars in the north who supported the view that Greenland was part of continental Europe.[34] The presence of continental
animals was one reason for this belief. The discovery of the "cold
coast" far to the north also must have confirmed this conviction.

In the Icelandic Annals for the year 1194, the scribe made the
following brief entry: "Svalbard was discovered." [35] The introduction to the *Landnamabok* reveals that Svalbard was four days' sail
north of Iceland at the north of the Hafsbotn (the Atlantic).[36]
Most investigators are agreed that Svalbard is the present Spitsbergen.[37] At the time of its discovery it must have appeared to be
part of the coast which connected Greenland with Europe. The
northern seafarers knew that such a land bridge had to be far
to the north. They also knew that it could not join with Europe
west of the White Sea and northern Russia.[38]

The early thirteenth-century *Historia Norwegiae* reported that

---

A.D. 1000–1600 (Minneapolis, 1964), 9–10; Gustav Storm, "Ginnungagap
i Mythologien og i Geografien," *Arkiv for Nordisk Filologi,* VI (1890),
340–50.

[34] Cf. Nansen, *In Northern Mists,* II, 35. See also Storm, "Ginnungagap,"
344–47.

[35] Hennig, *Terrae Incognitae,* II, 461.

[36] But only one day's sail to the uninhabited coast of Greenland. *Landnamabok,* II, 62. The same passage reveals that Iceland was considered "five
days' sail" from Ireland.

[37] Lethbridge (*Herdsmen and Hermits,* 109) holds that Svalbard was
probably Frans Joseph Fjord in East Greenland. This view is rejected in
favor of Spitsbergen by Hennig (*Terrae Incognitae,* II, 461–64). See also
Nansen, *In Northern Mists,* II, 166–68. Others such as Ashe (*Land to the
West,* 109–30) favor Jan Mayen Island; others, northeast Greenland. Cf.
Skelton *et al, Vinland Map and Tartar Relation,* 186–87.

[38] Snorre Sturlason, the Icelandic historian, reported a trading expedition to the White Sea in 1026. Concerning this Nansen (*In Northern Mists,*
II, 138) says: "Even if the voyage was not historical, the description of the
voyage and the place names along the route nevertheless show that these
regions were well known to Snorre's informants." Three other expeditions to this region are mentioned elsewhere, one in 1090, one in 1217,
and one in 1222. See *ibid.,* 138–40.

Greenland, which "forms the end of Europe towards the west, nearly touches the African islands where the returning ocean overflows." [39] This concept, first noted in some of the manuscripts of Nikulas' geographical treatise, continued to be accepted in the north. In a work of later but uncertain date, we are told: "Between Wineland and Greenland is Ginnungagap, it proceeds from the sea that is called 'Mare Oceanum,' which surrounds the whole world." [40]

The Icelandic term for the Atlantic was "Hafsbotn." This term need only be translated to be explained. It means bay or gulf of the ocean. There is perhaps no better indication of the prevalence of the northern concept of an outer and inner ocean than the common use of this term.

The *Historia Norwegiae* also reported strange people had been found by the Greenlanders on the other side of their land, on what must have been considered by the author to be the coast of the outer ocean:

> On the other side of the Greenlanders towards the north there have been found by hunters certain small people whom they call Skraelings; when these are struck while alive by weapons, their wounds turn white without blood, but when they are dead the blood scarsely stops running. But they have a complete lack of the metal iron; they use the tusks of marine animals for missiles and sharp stones for knives. [41]

Theodricus, a monk of Drontheim, wrote a Latin history of Norway (c. 1177–80) in which he told of the discovery of Iceland and the arrival there of Christianity. [42] The Danish historian Saxo Grammaticus (1150–1206) also discussed Iceland but did not comment on the sea beyond it. In his preface he praised the men of

[39] Nansen, *In Northern Mists*, II, 1, citing *Historia Norwegiae*. See Halldór Hermannsson, *Bibliography of the Sagas of the Kings of Norway*, in *Islandica*, III, (1910), 31.

[40] Nansen, *In Northern Mists*, II, 239. This work which Nansen refers to as *Gripla* is, he says, only known in a late ms. which dates from the first half of the seventeenth century.

[41] Nansen, *In Northern Mists*, II, 79.

[42] Thoroddsen, *Geschichte der Isländischen Geographie*, I, 58. See also Hermannsson, *Bibliography of the Sagas of the Kings of Norway*, 67. Theodricus' work is entitled *Historia de Antiquitate Regum Norwegiensium*.

Thule who accounted it "a delight to learn and to consign to remembrance the history of all nations, deeming it as great a glory to set forth the excellences of others as to display their own." Saxo was apparently not at all interested in Icelandic history itself, although that island did contain marvels which he could not resist reporting, including geysers, volcanoes, glaciers, and honest men.[43]

[43] Saxo Grammaticus, *Danish History,* trans. Oliver Elton (London, 1894), 5, 10–12. Re glaciers, Wright, *Geographic Lore,* 219, says: "This passage of Saxo has been cited as the earliest occasion in literature in which the motion of the glacial ice was recognized."

XII *Search, Light and Shadows*

HE ICELANDER Snorre Sturlason (1178–1241) was one of the breed used to justify the accounts by Giraldus Cambrensis and Saxo Grammaticus which indicated that Iceland had become the haven of honest men and good historians.[1] Snorre's *Heimskringla*, or "The World's Circle," was a monumental history of the Norse kings. It began, as did most medieval historical works, with a brief geographical discussion, and only differed from these in its emphasis on northern Europe.[2] The *Heimskringla* is a storehouse of information on Norse ships, but its primary interest to us is a matter of some debate.[3] In the "Saga of Olav Trygvason," it is reported that Leif Ericson "found Vinland the Good." [4] The next eight chapters concern the colonization of Vinland. Some editors of the text recognize these as a later insertion but consider that they were added by Snorre or an assistant during his lifetime.[5] If this is so, a full written account of the Vinland voyages and attempts at colonization appeared before 1250.

Another Scandinavian work of considerable importance is the *King's Mirror*, which appeared in Norway in the mid-thirteenth century. The author is not known, although Einar Gunnarsson, who became Archbishop of Nidaros in 1255, has been suggested.[6] Whoever the author, he appears to have done some traveling, to

---

[1] Of course Snorre has also been called "avaricious, ambitious and aspiring," but this has to do with political and economic activities beyond the scope of this investigation.

[2] Snorre Sturlason, *Heimskringla*, I, 1, ed. and trans. Erling Monsen and A. H. Smith (New York, 1932), 1–2.

[3] Cf. Brögger and Shetelig, *Viking Ships, passim.*

[4] Snorre Sturlason, *Heimskringla*, VII, 96.

[5] *Ibid.*, xviii, 188 n.

[6] Ingstad, *Land under the Pole Star*, 238.

have lived in Iceland, and possibly Greenland. He also was well-read. He believed in a spherical earth:

The earth-circle is round like a ball and is not equally near the sun at every point. But where the curved surface lies nearest the sun's path, there will the greatest heat be; and some of the lands that lie continuously under the unbroken rays cannot be inhabited.[7]

He also considered the extreme north to be uninhabitable and wrote that, if people lived on the other side of the earth, conditions there were reversed. He seemed to think that Hell was, in part at least, beneath the northern Atlantic since the volcanoes of Iceland had their origins in that infernal region.[8]

The *King's Mirror* was arranged as a conversation between father and son. The son was eager to learn of the world and life and to choose a profession. Upon hearing that the boy was considering a merchant's career, the father advised him:

Observe carefully how the sky is lighted, the course of the heavenly bodies, the grouping of the hours, and the points of the horizon. Learn also to mark the movements of the ocean and to discern how its turmoil ebbs and swells; for that is knowledge which all must possess who wish to trade abroad.[9]

The whales and other sea life to be found in the waters around Iceland and Greenland were described in great detail as were the Greenland ice floes. The father explained:

It has frequently happened that men . . . have been caught in the ice floes. Some of those who have been caught have perished; but others have got out again, and we have met some of these and have heard their accounts and tales. . . . Some have had to spend four days or five upon the ice before reaching land, and some even longer.

These ice floes have peculiar habits. Sometimes they lie as quiet as can be, though cut apart by creeks or large fjords; at other times they travel with a speed so swift and violent that a ship with a fair wind behind is not more speedy; and when once in motion,

---

[7] *King's Mirror*, VII, trans. Lawrence M. Larson (New York, 1917). See also *ibid.*, LVI.

[8] *Ibid.*, XIII, XIX, XXI.

[9] *Ibid.*, IV. Re navigation see especially *ibid.*, XXII, XXIII.

they travel as often against the wind as with it. There is also ice of a different shape which the Greenlanders call icebergs.[10]

The author of the *King's Mirror* was among those who felt that the presence of continental animals in Greenland indicated that it was part of a continent. Though the author did not say Europe specifically but "some mainland," he indicated that he felt Europe the logical candidate. He did not believe that there was land beyond Greenland, "only the great ocean which runs around the earth." Moreover, he had been told "by informed men" that Greenland bordered on the channel "through which the wide ocean rushes into the gap that lies between the land masses." [11] The gap, in this case, was the Atlantic Ocean.

In many ways the *King's Mirror* was a forthright, sensible combination of common sense, personal observation, and judicious scholarship, as well as a storehouse of information concerning Greenland. Just as the sagas, however, it remained in the province of the Scandinavians and was not translated into Latin or other vernaculars.

Whether the saga materials pertinent to our problem were in written form before A.D. 1250 is a debated point. If not, they were written down soon thereafter. The *Eyrbyggja Saga* was in written form before the end of the thirteenth century, as was the *Saga of the Greenlanders*, which was preserved in the *Flateyarbok*.[12] The latter tale gave much attention to the family of Eric the Red. Strangely, this was less true of the *Saga of Eric the Red*, preserved in two manuscripts, the older of which, the *Hauksbok*, dates from the fourteenth century. The saga which bore Eric's name emphasized Icelanders involved in the western voyages.

It is possible that some of the information contained in the Vinland sagas, either in written or oral form, filtered south; but, if such was the case, there is as yet no indication of any lasting impression. Perhaps the information was simply not accepted. De-

[10] *Ibid.*, XII, XVI.
[11] *Ibid.*, XVII, XIX.
[12] Cf. Parry, "The Vinland Story," 418: "The *Tale*, however, in its written form is older than the [fourteenth-century] codex in which it is preserved by at least a hundred years, probably considerably more."

bate as to the credibility of the saga narratives continues down to the present, as pointed out by J. H. Parry:

Opinion on the credibility of these narratives has varied a great deal. Some nineteenth-century enthusiasts—Rafn in the first and Horsford in the second half of the century, for examples—treated them with a credulity to which, probably, no early work of history is entitled. For many years, also, the *Tale of the Greenlanders* was considered the older and more authoritative text. In 1887 the trend was reversed by Gustav Storm, the learned editor of the Icelandic Annals, who gave reasons for preferring the *Hauksbok* narrative and cast grave doubts on the reliability of the *Flateyarbok*. In 1911 Fridtjof Nansen carried skepticism much further; Nansen was inclined to treat all the sagas as imaginative literature; or at least, as traditional tales, so overlaid with fiction and imported mythology as to have little claim to be regarded as historical. Little remained of the Vinland story when he had finished with it. Nansen's immense, and deserved, authority was not to be challenged lightly; but in 1921 G. M. Gathorne-Hardy began the work of careful reconstruction. Gathorne-Hardy pointed out that there was little ground for preferring one saga to the other, except for judgment, necessarily largely subjective, as to which of the accounts seemed more coherent and plausible. He admitted that both sagas, in the centuries which had elapsed between the events they described and their reduction to writing, had gathered accretions of myth and marvel, as a ship on a long passage gathers barnacles; but he thought that these accretions could be identified, distinguished from the central themes, and, so to speak, stripped away. There would remain two accounts of one series of events; accounts remarkable for their sober treatment and matter-of-fact detail, based to all appearance on historical fact, and in most respects reconcilable one with the other. Gathorne-Hardy's view of the sagas, in the main, prevails today.[13]

From the time of settlement, the Greenlanders supplemented their food supply with game from land and sea. Furs, ivory, walrus hide, falcons, eiderdown, and polar bears were valuable articles of trade. Many Greenlanders spent much of their time to the north and west beyond the main areas of settlement. With the passage of time this tendency appears to have increased. How many went how far how often cannot possibly be known. Most of the Canadian Arctic, however, was within their reach, and the

---

[13] *Ibid.* See also Magnusson and Palsson, *The Viking Sagas*, 30–35.

recently discovered Yale Vinland Map suggests a detailed and accurate knowledge of northern Greenland. The Vinland map also has an inscription which confirms a spiritually inspired expedition, that of a Bishop Eric whom the Icelandic Annals reported as setting out from Greenland for Vinland in 1121. We also learn from Icelandic sources that Greenlanders were still visiting Markland for timber in 1347. Presumably such voyages were frequent during the preceding 350 years.[14] What role, if any, Greenlanders played in the reputed Portuguese–Danish expedition to North America around 1470 is not known.

One of the most dramatic bits of evidence concerning the extension of the Greenlander's horizons is a Runic inscription found on the small island of Kingiktorsoak which had been placed there by three Greenlanders who "raised these marks and cleared land here on Saturday before Ascension week." This message is followed by a date which is variously interpreted as 1135, 1314, or 1333.[15] Whatever the date, these men were over eight hundred miles from home and well above the Arctic Circle in Baffin Bay, and they must have wintered in the area. There are other archaeological indications as well—beacons, cairns, and eiderduck nesting shelters—which indicate Greenlander penetration of the farther North and what must have been extensive contact with the Skraelings who preceded the Norse in the area.

One must concur with T. J. Oleson that "there can be no doubt that the relations between the medieval Greenlanders and the aborigines of America form a subject greatly in need of clarification. . . . For it was in Greenland and in the lands west of it that the Icelandic voyages had their most important and lasting effects. By comparison the Vinland voyages, so much publicized and often romanticized, were ephemeral ventures."[16] His bias is pro-

---

[14] For a listing of "Norse" stone houses and tombs reported on the Labrador coast, see Sir Wilfred Grenfell, *The Romance of Labrador* (New York, 1934), 69–71.

[15] Cf. *ibid.*, 56; Kaj Birket-Smith, *The Eskimos* (London, 1959), 14; Oleson, *Early Voyages*, 40; Nansen, *In Northern Mists*, I, 297; William Thalbitzer, *Two Runic Stones, from Greenland and Minnesota*, in *Smithsonian Miscellaneous Collections*, CXVI, no. 3 (1950–51), 13.

[16] Oleson, *The Norsemen in America*, 12.

gressively and obviously more apparent. One cannot help but rejoice, however, that in the late Oleson the Canadian Arctic had found an ardent and long overdue champion.

References in the sagas themselves and in other northern sources suggest at least occasional Greenland contact with more southerly regions, but one must again concur with Oleson that the evidence for continual contact with the Canadian Arctic is much more impressive. Exports from Greenland included hides of many animals not native to that country, such as wolf, glutton, lynx, sable, ermine, otter, beaver, black bear, and elk, all northern in provenance.

Evidence of the introduction into the European north, however temporary, of maize, turkeys, or other American products from more southerly regions would be fairly conclusive indication of European contacts below the St. Lawrence, but as yet no northern pictorial or sculptural representation of maize dating before the Age of Discovery has been found which is not more challenged than accepted,[17] and no textual description is definitive. To date, moreover, the search for turkey bones in Europe has led primarily to the bones of peacocks.[18] Excavations in Greenland itself have unearthed a piece of anthracite coal which might have come from Rhode Island, an Indian arrow tip with wider geographic possibilities as to source, and a plant specimen, *Iridace Sisyrhynchium Angustifolium*, native to the American temperate zone but not to Greenland.[19]

Greenland's trade flourished, largely due to the exploitation of regions to the west and north. Because of the falcons it exported, Greenland was a well-known country to the emperor Frederick II, who about 1244 produced a volume on the art of falconry entitled *De Arte Venandi cum Avibus*. It was so well known in fact

---

[17] For example, the maize-like fruit depicted by Gislebertus, the sculptor of Autun cathedral.

[18] This at any rate is what turkey bones reportedly found in a thirteenth-century context in Switzerland turned out to be. Cf., however, T. Christensen, "Viking and Turkeys," included in Goodwin, *The Truth about Leif Ericsson*, 325–27.

[19] Oleson, *Early Voyages*, 91. Concerning the coal, one wonders if one of its companion pieces inspired the account of burning ice appearing in the Meregarto.

that he located Iceland in reference to Greenland rather than the other way around.[20] In 1261, during the reign of Haakon Haakonsson, the Greenlanders became subject to the Norwegian crown, and trade with Greenland became a royal monopoly.[21] During the next century trading and contact with Norway fell off, with the Black Death's grim trek across Europe and with Hanseatic control of Bergen as contributing factors.

By 1350 the smaller and more northerly of the settlements on Greenland's east coast were apparently abandoned. By 1400, or shortly thereafter, the Roman Catholic Church itself seemed to have lost interest in its extreme western outposts.[22] The Eastern Settlement, which although so-called was only comparatively eastern (being on the southwestern coast), struggled to maintain existence and identity well into the sixteenth century. In 1540, an Icelandic ship, blown off course, took shelter in a Greenland fjord where the crew found a dead man lying face downward on the ground. "On his head was a hood, well made, and [he was] otherwise clothed both in frieze cloth and sealskin. Near him lay a sheath knife, much worn and eaten away." [23] Somewhere in the region, other Greenlanders may have still been living, but no search was made. The next recorded visitors found no Norse.

[20] Frederick II, *The Art of Falconry*, II, 4. (Stanford, 1961). Cf. Oleson, *Early Voyages*, 93.

[21] Cf. *The Saga of Hacon, Hacon's Son*, trans. G. Vigfusson (London, 1894), 333–34 for the year 1261: "That autumn . . . [messengers] brought word from Greenland that they had accepted the scatt-tax, and also that all manslayings should be atoned for to the king, . . . whether they were slain in the inhabited land or in the north country. This was to hold too though men set up their abode to the farthest north under the pole star; there too the king had the right to claim the thane-fine for them."

[22] Cf. Knut Gjerset, *History of the Norwegian People* (New York, 1915), 201–204; Ingstad, *Land Under the Pole Star*, 208–209; Jones, *Norse Atlantic Saga*, 62–63. For a chronological listing of latter-day references to the Greenland colonists, from 1341 to 1426, see Ingstad, *Land Under the Pole Star*, 287–88. See also the "Chronology of Western Voyages," c. 1025 to 1570, in Mowat, *Westviking*, 476–77.

[23] Mowat, *Westviking*, 302; Oxenstierna, *The Norsemen*, 252. Norlund has this to report of John Davis:

In 1585 he ran into Godthaab Fjord, the West Settlement of the Norsemen, but without realising that it was Greenland he had reached. During the succeeding years he repeatedly touched at the west coast, and in 1586 found on an island in Godthaab Fjord (Gil-

Concerning the disappearance of the Norse settlements on Greenland, T. J. Oleson has noted:

Many ingenious theories have been advanced to explain it: that the Icelanders [on Greenland] were exterminated by aborigines or by pirates in bloody warfare; that malnutrition and physical degeneration brought the race to an end; that its vitality was destroyed by consanguineous marriages; that climatic deterioration made husbandry no longer possible; that epidemics killed the people, while the worms of a butterfly (*Agrotis occulta*) destroyed vegetation. Some of these theories lack any basis in evidence, some are fantastic, and none has much to recommend it.[24]

Oleson's solution is fundamentally simple: intermixture with the aborigines.[25]

The Skraelings had begun to infiltrate the area during the thirteenth century; but many Europeans survived as a type in the Eastern Settlement late in the fifteenth century. It would appear therefore that, although Oleson's arguments may have much validity, his is far from being a total answer. Many of the theories which he dismisses may point at least to contributory factors. Furthermore, some Europeans may have gone native, while others clung to the settlement and their heritage until the end found them inbred and bred out.

---

bert Sound) a grave in which several people had been buried, covered only with sealskin, over which a cross had been laid. Presumably the grave had been built of stones like those of the Eskimos, but the cross shows that they were Christian people, and the record is remarkable. The West Settlement had been abandoned 200 years earlier, and we cannot say if the people in the Eskimo-like grave were Greenland Norsemen or more likely European whalers of unknown nationality. Ships can very well have called at Greenland, and also visited the Norse regions, in both the fifteenth and the sixteenth centuries without the fact becoming common knowledge in Europe.
See Poul Norlund, *Viking Settlers in Greenland* (London, 1936), 152–53.

[24] Oleson, *The Norsemen in America*, 9. The role of climate and its effect upon the Greenland settlement has been much discussed. Those interested might begin with John Lear, "What Did the Norsemen Discover?," *Saturday Review* (November 6, 1965), 49–52; and the passages which figure prominently in Mr. Lear's discussion found in Rachel Carson, *The Sea Around Us* (New York, 1951), 178–87.

[25] Cf. Jacob Fried, *A Survey of the Aboriginal Populations of Quebec and Labrador* (Montreal, 1955); L. Oschinsky, *The Most Ancient Eskimos* (Ottawa, 1964).

The search for the lost colonists of Greenland, especially those who disappeared in the fourteenth century, has long been underway. There is a possibility that the settlers gave up their faith and went to join the people of America. Recent discovery of a possible Norse settlement in northern Quebec has revived speculation. What the end result of current excavation, under the auspices of the Nordic Studies Center at the Université de Laval in Quebec, will be, and whether discoveries on the west coast of Ungava Bay and in the interior of Ungava Peninsula contribute to our knowledge of the latter-day Greenlander's activity, remains to be seen.[26]

The search for Norse-Eskimos has been an involved one with many reported successes, not all of which have found acceptance. Hovgaard reported that Eskimo traditions, which he acknowledged were "mere traditions," pointed to "the existence in Baffin Land, in perhaps not very remote times, of a hybrid tribe of Eskimos, who might well, according to the description, be descendants of the old Norse-Eskimo tribes of Greenland." He postulated the later westward migration of these people and connected them with the "Blond Eskimos" located by Stefansson on Victoria Island.[27] Stefansson's data in this connection, however, has not gone unchallenged. The most likely, or at any rate the least challenged, evidences of intermixture have been found on Greenland itself. The scope of this book, however, precludes our joining in the search.

[26] Cf. "Important Discoveries in Quebec," *N.E.A.R.A. Newsletter,* II (March, 1967), 6–7.

[27] Hovgaard, *Voyages of the Norsemen,* 48–50. See Vilhjalmur Stefansson, *My Life with the Eskimos* (New York, 1913), 191–202.

XIII *On the Map*

IT IS ONE of the ironies of history that as merchants and seamen reputedly paid less attention to Greenland and the strug-
gling Norse colonists, the scholars and especially the cartographers
became more cognizant of it. Many map-makers, sifting bits of
knowledge from earlier centuries, attempted to decide how it fit
into the world picture. It is, of course, possible and even likely that
the information from earlier centuries was occasionally buttressed
by more contemporary reports.

Oleson contended that, although Greenland's contact with Europe is thought to have grown weaker by the fifteenth century,
this might be explained by the fact that the Icelandic Annals were
not kept after 1430. He noted that "Greenland . . . seems to have
been better known than ever in Europe, if we are to judge by its
representation on fifteenth century maps." [1] The Yale Vinland Map
makes the case even stronger.

On the maps and in the records, Greenland was frequently
ascribed features of terrain, climate, flora and fauna more attribut-
able to regions adjacent to it, or to regions the products of which
arrived in Europe via Greenland. References to a climate milder
than that of Iceland or Norway, to all kinds of fruit, to wheat
fields and large tracts of woodland undoubtedly belong in this
category. [2]

Greenland was depicted cartographically as an extension of
Europe or as an island off the coast of Asia. The eastern islands
of the Canadian Arctic appeared as the Falcon Islands off eastern
Asia. A variety of names also were applied to Greenland or to
contiguous areas. It would seem that Greenland was "Gallandia"

[1] Oleson, *Norsemen in America*, 19.
[2] Oleson, *Early Voyages*, 92.

to Fredrick II. A Greenland, which more specifically appears to be Baffin Island, is called Harmüsa by the Arab writer Abu'l-Hasan 'Ali Ibn Sa'id, who referred to the frequent importation of polar bear pelts in Egypt. The attributes of the Greenland area were at times understandably applied to Iceland, or even to Norway since it was, after all, Norwegian territory. The names Rozeya and Ganzmir on the map of Henry of Mayence seem to apply to Greenland regions.[3] Roseya also appeared as a name for Greenland on the late thirteenth-century Hereford map with Ganzmir in the vicinity. Albania, apparently derived from the Hvitraman-naland of the sagas, also seems to refer to Greenland or to Asian territory considered adjacent to it.[4]

T. J. Oleson had the following to say concerning maps which are later in time than our established limit of A.D. 1250, but which may, nevertheless be based on information which made its way eastward and southward before the mid-thirteenth century:

Two maps, one from the fourteenth century and one from the fifteenth, amply testify to the knowledge of the lands of America which were peopled by the Icelanders at this time. The first is the Medici marine chart from 1351. This shows Greenland as an extension of Norway but nothing beyond it. On the other hand the second map, the Genoa world map from 1447 or 1457, shows the whole of the eastern Canadian Arctic. This shows Norway, and west of it a peninsula which can only be Greenland. Lelewel thought he could read the name Grinland but this is not now possible because the inscription has faded so much. This, however, is of little consequence as there is pictured on it a polar bear which can only refer to Greenland. Next to it is a bay filled with many islands and then a large land mass on which is depicted a fox. This must be Baffin Island, which is recorded in the sagas as being the land of foxes. West of it, with two or three islands, is Hudson Bay.

In the fifteenth century the Dane, Claudius Clavus Swart, drew at least two maps of Greenland. The first of these was made during the years 1413–1427. The second is after 1450. On it is the inscription: "Norway possesses eighteen islands which in the winter are because of ice contiguous to the mainland and are seldom separated from it unless the summer is very hot." Again, Nicolaus Germanus, after the year 1466, drew a world map on which he shows Green-

---

[3] Oleson, *Norsemen in America*, 19.
[4] Oleson, *Early Voyages*, 93–98.

land. He must have obtained his information from the Greenlanders, for on the map is shown an *insula glaciei* which can only be Newfoundland and points to knowledge derived from Greenland of the ice in the Labrador current.[5]

The concept of Greenland as a peninsular extension of Europe reaching far to the west seems to have been introduced into southern cartography by Claudius Clavus Swart, a Dane who visited Rome about 1424. This cultural lag in the dissemination of information justifies somewhat our use of later maps to illustrate information gleaned in earlier periods. It is also possible that the information which Clavus dispensed may have included concepts no longer held in the northern regions. The gap between the bookman and the boatman was still a wide one.[6]

The periplus of the ancient must have been, occasionally, also accompanied by a sea chart. These charts, however, have not survived, at least, not any of comparable dates. Charles Hapgood has theorized that some of the portolano maps of the fourteenth, fifteenth, and sixteenth centuries were based on prototypes preclassical in origin; he and his followers may have no difficulty in imagining hundreds of intermediary exempla, but, unfortunately, to date no one has been able to produce the necessary concrete examples.[7] No sailing charts antedating the second half of the thirteenth century are known to have survived. Miss Eva G. R. Taylor has said that the use of sea charts or maps during the classical and medieval periods is probable.[8] One must concur. R. A. Skelton has pointed out that Norse seamen were without quadrant, astrolabe, magnetic compass, or sea charts.[9] This is an act of faith based upon evidence. Evidence, like sand, not only is adapted to sifting but can shift. When Skelton said that the Norse seaman, on the longer Atlantic passages, "who was unaware of magnetic variation, could not have obtained as good determinations of position by the compass (even if he had had it) as he did by other meth-

---

[5] *Ibid.*, 98.
[6] R. A. Skelton, *The European Image and the Mapping of America, A.D. 1000–1600* (Minneapolis, 1964), 11.
[7] Cf. Hapgood, *Maps of the Ancient Sea Kings, passim.*
[8] Taylor, *Haven-finding Art,* 55–57.
[9] Skelton, *et al., Vinland Map and Tartar Relation,* 168–79.

ods," he was, to preserve the simile, upon firmer ground.[10] This is, in fact, an important point. The compass was an aid rather than a prerequisite to the production of sailing charts or maps.

Farley Mowat has taken the position that sea charts were indeed used by the Norse:

> Although no original Norse charts have been recovered, some of them must have survived until relatively recent times. The Stefansson Map, which was drawn from ancient Icelandic sources, could have been derived only from the data laid down in visual form by voyagers who had charted Labrador and Newfoundland.
>
> Norse charts probably showed courses in terms of airts, and distances in some conventionalized manner. Relative latitudes would doubtless have been indicated. Coasts were probably sketched in roughly. As with many primitive charts, the scale was probably not constant over the whole drawing. Sections which contained nothing of special interest to the navigator would have been much compressed in area and generally simplified in treatment.
>
> Charts were perhaps not as valuable to Norse navigators as oral sailing directions were. These were of vital importance, as we know by their frequent inclusion in the saga accounts. A typical set of sailing instructions from the sagas gives: (1) The departure landmark; (2) The directions, in airts; (3) The distance, out of sight of land; (4) The arrival landmarks.[11]

In this connection, it is worth noting that, in 1889, A. E. Nordenskiöld postulated that among the cartographic resources existing in Italy around 1400 there had been a "map of the Scandinavian peninsula, Iceland, and Greenland, composed ere the northern mariners became acquainted with the use of the compass, perhaps in the beginning of the thirteenth century." [12] Once again, probability at least brings us back within our period.

At least three men of the sixteenth and seventeenth centuries

[10] *Ibid.*, 169.

[11] Mowat, *Westviking*, 361–62.

[12] A. E. Nordenskiöld, *Facsimile Atlas to the Early History of Cartography* (Stockholm, 1889), 38. Cf. Skelton *et al.*, *Vinland Map*, 167. Those interested in this problem will also find the following articles pertinent: Heinrich Winter, "The Origin of the Sea Chart," *Imago Mundi*, VIII (1951), 39–41; Heinrich Winter, "The True Position of Hermann Wagner in the Controversy of the Compass Chart," *Imago Mundi*, V (1948), 21–26; and Richard Uhden, "Die antiken Grundlagen der mittelalterlichen Seekarten," *Imago Mundi*, I (1935), 1–19.

were to produce maps which, according to their testimony, collated contemporary knowledge with that which they had gleaned from ancient northern maps and records. Sigurdur Stefánsson, an Icelandic schoolmaster, produced his map in 1579 (although the surviving copy apparently dates from about 1590). The map of the Danish bishop Hans Poulson Resen dates from 1605, and that of the Icelandic bishop Gudbrandur Thorlaksson from 1606. He was vague as to their placement, but Thorlaksson knew, although many of his day had forgotten, that both the Eastern and Western Settlements of the Norse in Greenland were to the west of Cape Farewell.[13] The Stefánsson map avoided the issue, and it has been suggested that in this instance the cartographer distrusted his source. Resen has the settlements placed correctly.

Whether Resen's map presented a geographical design copied from Stefánsson or both had a common source or sources need not concern us. At any rate, Resen claimed to have seen a medieval Icelandic map. Whatever the doubts, as Skelton points out: "The strongly marked 'promontory of Vinland' has no parallel in 16th century maps." Helge Ingstad's, and his wife's, discoveries in northern Newfoundland seem to demonstrate that the sources for these later maps not only existed but were historically reliable.

Arlington H. Mallery, in his *Lost America*, one of the volumes belonging to the fascinating fringe of pre-Columbian scholarship, noted that:

Writing sometime around 1605, Icelandic historian Bjorn Jonsson (1574–1655) declared: "Sir Erlend Thordsen, a priest in the parish of Staden, Iceland, in the year 1568, obtained from abroad the geographical chart of that Albania or Land of the White Man (Vitramannaland) which is situated opposite Vinland the Good and which the merchants formerly called Hibernia Major or Irland Mikla. The chart had shown accurately all those tracts of land . . . and the boundaries of Markland, together with Greenland.[14]

Mallery also referred to a chart produced in 1605 by Christiano Friseo which had the following legend in Latin: "Greenland and nearby regions toward the North and West from an ancient map

[13] Cf. Skelton, *The European Image*, 23–24. These maps are all reproduced in Skelton *et al*, *Vinland Map*.

[14] Arlington H. Mallery, *Lost America* (Columbus, Ohio, 1951), 158.

drawn in a crude manner many hundred years ago in Iceland, in which they were then known lands, together with nautical observations made in our own time." [15]

Not until the thirteenth century do we find a specific reference to a sea chart presumably of the portolano type. In 1270 Louis IX of France was shown one after a storm in the Mediterranean.[16] The earliest surviving portolano, also concerned with the Mediterranean, is the Carte Pisane, which dates from approximately the same time. The first dated chart was produced in Genoa in 1311.[17] There is every indication, however, that these charts represent older traditions involving both content and techniques which date back at least to the period we have under study. The Yale Vinland Map does not belong to the portolano tradition. It has been proclaimed in fact that it belongs to none.[18] The Vinland Map, the authenticity of which appears to be fairly well established (in spite of challenges from such reputable critics as G. R. Crone and E. G. R. Taylor), however, does serve as latter-day testimony to earlier knowledge and events.[19]

[15] *Ibid.*, 157.

[16] E. G. R. Taylor and M. W. Ritchey, *The Geometrical Seaman* (London, 1962), 23.

[17] Leo Bagrow, *History of Cartography*, as revised and enlarged by R. A. Skelton (London, 1964), 63.

[18] Cf. Carlos Sanz, "Un mapa del mundo verdaderamente importante en la famosa Universidad de Yale," *Boletín de la Real Sociedad Geografica*, CII (1966), 55. This article examines the Henricus Martellus Germanus map of 1490 and devotes only a portion of the last page to the Vinland. Señor Sanz's disclaimer seems, however, to be more than partially met by the article by Thomas Goldstein, "Conceptual Patterns Underlying the Vinland Map," *Renaissance News*, XIX (1966), 321–31.

[19] Cf. G. R. Crone, "How Authentic is the 'Vinland Map,'" *Encounter*, XXVI (February, 1966), 75–78; G. R. Crone, "The Vinland Map Geographically Considered," *Geographical Journal*, CXXXII (March, 1966), 75–80. Crone argues that the map is after 1486 and probably post-Columbian and, while conceding that the text may not be later than 1490, asks if the map is an integral part of the whole. Concerning Greenland he says: "With the instruments and techniques of those [early fifteenth-century] days no such accurate outline would have resulted." R. A. Skelton answers Crone in "Interpreting the Vinland Map," *Encounter*, XXVI (June, 1966), 93. Dr. E. G. R. Taylor's doubting views appear in a summary by M. W. Richey, "The Vinland Map," *Journal of the Institute of Navigation*, XIX (January, 1966), 124–25. Cf. also W. H. Hobbs, "Zeno and the Cartog-

J. H. Parry has written that "the body of internal evidence supporting the integrity and authenticity of the map and the early date assigned to it seems overwhelming." [20] Thomas Goldstein has agreed, proclaiming it "a little fanciful to question their [Skelton, Marston, and Painter] cautious conclusion that the authenticity can in effect be accepted." Goldstein has succeeded admirably in placing the Vinland Map within both a historical and cartographical framework. He acknowledges that, cartographically, nothing actually new has been revealed concerning the Norse and the New World. He feels, however, that it might be described as the first modern map, based upon a new global concept. It represents the North Atlantic as an entity rather than as an appendage, giving the oceanic surface of the earth its proper place in the scheme of a significant global context. "*The Vinland map*," Goldstein has written (and his italics acknowledge the quotability of the passage), *in other words, raises the Oceanic parts of the earth to a level of equal importance with the traditional sphere of the 'habitable land.' Its emphasis (in terms of the unprecedented or unusual) is on the maritime areas of the globe.*" [21] The ocean is portrayed as a "*potential waterway linking the two ends of the habitable world.*" According to Goldstein, the Vinland Map was the "explicit cartographic expression of a new type of geographic thought, which assumed the complete accessibility of the globe, thereby extending the human habitat from its tradition-bound limitations to the very ends of the earth." [22] Brendan, Leif, and many other earlier northern mariners were finally in a position to say "I told you so."

The problem as to the precise locale of production and the circumstances which culminated in the Vinland Map, once again, need not concern us; nor need we enter the debate as to the exact relationship of the Vinland Map to the lost Toscanelli map, other than to note that Goldstein suggested an affinity. [23] There are, however,

---

raphy of Greenland," *Imago Mundi*, VI (1949), 15–19. As for the possibility of outside help, see Leo Bagrow, "Eskimo Maps," *Imago Mundi*, V (1948), 92.

[20] Parry, "The Vinland Story."

[21] Goldstein, "Conceptual Patterns and the Vinland Map," 322–23.

[22] *Ibid.*, 327.

[23] *Ibid.*, 331.

other aspects of the map which lead us again back into our period. The appearance of the "Magnae Insulae Beati Brendani, Branziliae dictae," as distant from Spain as Greenland is from the British Isles, and the obvious suggestion that Brendan's Island(s) and Brazil have an onomastic relationship (Brandani insulae > Branziliae > Brãziliae > Braziliae > Brazil) has intriguing possibilities.[24]

More important for our purposes, of course, are the inscriptions found on the map concerning Vinland itself. Next to the island designated as Vinland is the following inscription: "Island of Vinland, discovered by Bjarni and Leif in company." It appears beside a large tripartite island far to the west. The three sections may be considered to represent the Helluland, Markland, and Vinland of the sagas, with Vinland being used as a name for the entire area (although such an equation certainly need not be insisted upon). A longer inscription placed on the map above Vinland and Greenland has been translated as follows:

By God's will, after a long voyage from the island of Greenland to the south toward the most distant remaining parts of the western ocean sea, sailing southward amidst the ice, the companions Bjarni and Leif Eiriksson discovered a new land, extremely fertile and even having vines, the which island they named Vinland. Eric, [Henricus] legate of the Apostolic See and bishop of Greenland and the neighboring regions, arrived in this truly vast and very rich land, in the name of Almighty God, in the last year of our most blessed father Pascal, remained a long time in both summer and winter, and later returned northeastward toward Greenland and then proceeded [i.e. home to Europe?] in most humble obedience to the will of his superiors.[25]

Skelton noted that reference is made in the inscription to two distinct historical events, the voyage of discovery by Bjarni and Leif and the protracted visit in Vinland by Bishop Eric Gnupsson, beginning in 1117.[26] Since the Icelandic Annals referred to the bishop's voyage to Vinland as taking place in 1121, either one of the dates is in error or there were two voyages. The latter solution is the least likely, although it should be noted that the inscription does

---

[24] Cf. Skelton *et al*, *Vinland Map*, 138. Crone in "How Authentic is the 'Vinland Map,'" 77, suggests simple elision: i.e. "Bran [dan Bra] zilia.

[25] Skelton *et al.*, *Vinland Map*, 140.

[26] *Ibid.*, 140, 223–26, 257–61.

not specifically say where Bishop Eric proceeded "in most humble obedience to the will of his superiors" after his return to Greenland from his 1117 trip. If one of the dates is in error, the consensus is almost unanimous in favor of accepting the 1117 date. As Samuel Thorne pointed out in his review of the Yale volume, 1117 fits better into Greenland ecclesiastical records. The Vinland Map may not serve to indicate precisely the area of Norse settlement, but to quote Thorne, whose verdict is shared by most: "The caption about Bishop Eirik's visit to Vinland may be accepted as historically authentic, and seems to confirm a twelfth century Norse settlement in Vinland." [27] Such testimony cannot fail to give encouragement to Helge and Anne Ingstad,[28] to Farley Mowat, to Frederick J. Pohl, and to hundreds of others searching for the excavatable remains of Norse settlements on the North American coast. European libraries and American soils will be sifted. The search for relics and records will go on at an accelerated pace. The Newport tower will be asked again to share its secrets; mooring holes will be fondly fingered; and many will continue to hope that the Kensington stone will rise, or, at the least, be raised, again.[29]

[27] Samuel Thorne, "Record of a Visit from the Vikings," *Saturday Review* (October, 1965), 48.

[28] Concerning Ingstad's views on the Vinland Map, as well as a summary of his Newfoundland excavations, see Ahlman, "Rediscovering Vinland," 187–90.

[29] Fortunately again, this too is beyond our period. Although most reputable authorities have agreed that the Kensington Stone is not genuine, some still take comfort and preserve hope because of the words of Thalbitzer, *Two Runic Stones,* 53: "After all, the anomalies of this inscription are no more remarkable than those of the Kingigtorssuag stone from Greenland, which is genuine."

XIV *Hither to Yon*

GIRALDUS CAMBRENSIS (Gerald of Wales, 1146–1222), the much traveled, multi-lingual, voluminous reporter of his contemporaries and their world, wrote much which receives not only less attention than he expected, but, unfortunately, less than it deserves. Among his legacies to posterity is a geographical work of considerable value, the *Topographia Hibernica*. The data he presented regarding tides in the Irish Sea showed that he or someone else had devoted quite a bit of time to observation. He, unlike some of his contemporaries, was quite sure that the moon (and not equatorial ocean current, etc.) was responsible for tides.[1] In this connection, it should be noted that the oldest surviving tide table, which is one for "Flod at London Brigge," dates from this same period (i.e. late twelfth or early thirteenth century).[2]

In the course of his treatise, Giraldus commented upon the islands near Ireland. Spain was to the south of Ireland, Britain to the east, "only ocean" to the west, and Iceland was three days' sail to the north.[3] Later he added that there were Orcades, "Incades" (Shetlands?), and many other islands in the north; these were presumably not mentioned earlier because of their smaller size. Among the "other islands" was one which was named Phantastica because when first observed it persisted in moving about, which gave rise to the rumor that it really was a whale or other marine monster. It had, however, since been stabilized.[4]

Iceland, wrote Giraldus, was inhabited by truthful people with a bishop for a king. Thunderstorms were rare there, but this blessing was balanced by the presence of volcanoes. Somewhere in the vi-

---

[1] Giraldus Cambrensis, *Topographia Hibernica*, II, 2–3, ed. James F. Dimock, Vol. V. of *Opera*, (London, 1867).

[2] Taylor, *Haven-finding Art*, 23, 136.

[3] Giraldus Cambrensis, *Topographia Hibernica*, I, 1: "maxima Yslandia."

[4] *Ibid.*, II, 11–12.

cinity there was also a great whirlpool which made sailing difficult.[5]

Thule posed a problem for Giraldus. No one in his acquaintance
knew anything about it, although he found it referred to in the
works of Solinus, Virgil, Isidore, and Orosius. Since he had noticed
that St. Augustine mentioned an island of India with a strikingly
similar name, Giraldus jokingly suggested that "the same island
would appear to be in India also." [6] Unknown to Giraldus, some of
his scholastic colleagues had already, and more seriously, made this
identification. Many characteristics of the "Indian" island had been
attached to the island of Thule which had refused to remain associated with a commonplace Iceland and was once again afloat in a
sea of marvels.[7]

The English scholar Alexander Neckam (d. 1230) was not concerned with the Atlantic West at all. His popular encyclopaedia of
scientific knowledge, *De Naturis Rerum*, did offer the reader some
information on the sea in general. The sea derived its saltiness from
the equatorial ocean, where it was formed by the heat of the sun
and other planets.[8] The tides presented an insoluble problem which
vexed the "moderns" just as it had the ancients. The earth was a
sphere of land and water. Why did not the sea, so constantly being
filled, get to be higher than the land? Neckam's answer in this case
was unique. The sea was the "grave of the waters" and its level did
grow continually higher; in fact it was already visibly higher (*ut
visus docet*) than the earth and only the will of God kept back the
flood.[9] Neckam did not explain his *ut visus docet* but his common
sense reasoning is easy to reconstruct if it is assumed that he was
not completely convinced of the spherical surface of the earth. On
a flat earth it would have become "visibly" apparent that the sea
was higher than the land if one watched a ship sail out of sight over
the crest of the bulbous ocean.

One item in Neckam's work is of especial interest. Although he

[5] *Ibid.*, II, 13–14.

[6] *Ibid.*, II, 17.

[7] See Cassidy, "The Voyage of an Island," 595–602.

[8] Alexander Neckam, *De Naturis Rerum Libri Duo*, II, 1, ed. Thomas
Wright (London, 1863). Cf. also *De Laudibus Divinae Sapientiae*, III,
75–80, in same volume.

[9] Neckam, *De Naturis Rerum*, II, 16–17, 49.

thought that sailing should be avoided whenever possible (one crossing of the English channel had provided him his fill), he was aware of the principle of the magnet and that sailors had a magnetic needle which indicated north.[10] This is the first known reference to the use of the compass in the west. This reference in Neckam, which can be dated about 1187, was followed a few years later (c. 1206) by a more detailed account in the pages of Guiot de Provins' *La Bible*.[11]

The compass appears to have been used earlier in the Atlantic than in the Mediterranean. Here it can be argued that use of and knowledge of are not synonymous and that there was less need of a compass in the latter area. It has been claimed, nevertheless, that the Norse compass, a magnet floating in a wooden bowl, was introduced into the Mediterranean before the end of the eleventh century by the Norman conquerors of southern Italy and Sicily, was developed into a more sophisticated instrument at Amalfi, and spread from there. The earliest datable portolano charts, usually associated with the use of the compass at sea, are of Mediterranean vintage.[12]

Before leaving the twelfth century, and before allowing an idiosyncratic scholastic current to take us swirling south to that intellectual maelstrom where Norse and Arab met, we might, for the sake of completeness, take a brief look at some non-historical voyagers. One came from Wales, as did Giraldus, and was reputedly a contemporary of his.

There is a shaky tradition that the Welsh, under a Prince Madoc, established a colony in the New World at the end of the twelfth century.

After the death of Owen Guyneth, his sonnes fell at debate who should inherit after him. . . . Madoc another of Owen Guyneth his sonnes left the land in contention betwixt his brethren, prepared certain ships, with men and munition, and sought adventures by Seas, sailing

---

[10] *Ibid.*, II, 19, 98.

[11] Guiot de Provins, *La Bible*, II, 632–54, in *Les Oeuvres de Guiot de Provins*, ed. John Orr (Manchester, 1915). For a discussion of these and other early notices of the compass see Taylor, *Haven-finding Art*, 94–96. See also Taylor and Richey, *The Geometrical Seaman*, 19–33.

[12] Bagrow, *History of Cartography*, 62.

West, and leaving the coast of Ireland so farre North, that he came unto a land unknowen, where he saw many strange things.

. . . . . .

Of the voyage and returne of this Madoc there be many fables fained, *as the common people doe use in distance of place and length of time rather to augment then to diminish:* but sure it is there he was. And after he had returned home, and declared the pleasant and fruitful countreys that he had seene without inhabitants, and upon the contrary part, for what barren & wild ground his brethren and nephewes did murther one another, he prepared a number of ships and got with him such men and women as were desirous to live in quietnesse; and taking leave of his friends, tooke his journey thitherward againe. . . .[13]

This story first appeared in an edition of Caradoc's *History of Wales* published by David Powell in 1584. Caradoc, however, died c. 1157, and this later addition is attributed to Guttun Owen, a Welsh bard (c. 1480) who reputedly found it in an abbey register. A section from a Welsh poem written c. 1477 also alludes to Madoc:

> Madoc I am the sonne of Owen Gwynedd
> With stature large and comely grace adorned:
> No lands at home nor store of wealth me please,
> My minde was whole to search the Ocean seas.[14]

It is easier, and safer, to admit Madoc's existence in fable than to attempt to establish his historicity.[15] The presence of such a tradition, however, would be another indication that Celtic interest in seafaring and in lands to the west did not die out completely. Vestiges of the Irish *Imrama* continued to be part of the medieval cultural picture, not only through the various saints' lives and the divers accounts of the voyages of St. Brendan the Navigator, but in much of medieval romance.

One finds, for example, in the twelfth-century *Romance of Tristram and Ysolt* by Thomas of Britain mariners, storm-tossed and driven far out to sea, who finally realized that the ocean was an

[13] Richard Hakluyt, *Principal Navigations Voyages Traffiques & Discoveries of the English Nation* (New York, 1904), VII, 133–34. Italics are this author's.

[14] *Ibid.*, 135.

[15] Cf. George Catlin, *North America Indians* (Edinburgh, 1926), I, 105–107, 231–32; II, 295–98.

agent of God and was preventing them from reaching the desired destination because they had sinned.[16] Later the wounded Tristram asked to be put in a rudderless boat: "Therefore will I depart hence, wheresoever God may suffer me to go according to his mercy and my need."

> Therewith was a vessel garnished with victual enough and whatso him needed: and . . . he took the sea, and all they that abode after prayed that God would guard him and pity him. And he was driven on the sea, what by wind and what by flood, so long that he wist not whither he went. . . .[17]

This same romance also reveals the pervasive influence which Arabic culture was beginning to have upon western thought. We find Tristram saying: "My kin and friends know not whither I am become nor if I be quick or dead, for when I departed I purposed to fare unto Spain, for I was fain to learn the lore of the stars and hidden matters." [18]

The Arab geographer Idrisi was born about 1100, possibly in

---

[16] Thomas of Britain, *The Romance of Tristram and Ysolt*, trans. Roger S. Loomis (New York, 1951), 25–26.

> For when they that had carried him away were well nigh arrived in their land, there came a sharp wind into their sail with such tempest and tide that they had been lost had they not hastily let drop the sail. The whole sea was stirred with grievous waves, it hailed and rained and thundered and lightened: the mast was high and the sea deep, and the ship rolled for the storm so that none might stand on foot, and they let the ship drive before the wind. All moaned and feared, wept and cried wildly . . . and all weened that they must perish, for that the wind drave them passing hard. A sennight the tempest smote and drave them that they saw no land, and even when the wind abated they had as much fear and distress, for they wist not how they might win to any land or haven. Then said they all unto the captain:
>
> "All this storm and peril and labor that we have endured befell us of our own desert, for that we have sinned. . . ."

[17] *Ibid.*, 80–83.

[18] *Ibid.*, 88. Another twelfth-century Anglo-Norman troubadour, Benoit, has an extensive geographical introduction to his *Chronique des Ducs de Normandie* based primarily upon Isidore. Cf. Benoit, *Chronique des Ducs de Normandie*, 1–772, ed. Francisque Michel (Paris, 1836). A great many of the medieval chroniclers begin their accounts with brief geographical discussions. Our thanks to Dr. Arda Walker who called this one to our attention.

Morocco. His travels took him throughout and beyond the Moslem world. He had been to France and England, to Byzantium and into Central Asia. Educated at Cordova, he became known for his learning, and was invited to the court of the Norman king, Roger II, of Sicily. Roger Guiscard became his patron, and Idrisi appears to have served him well for the rest of his life.

Roger was interested in navigation and geography, and his kingdom was a gathering place for merchants, seamen, pilgrims, crusaders, and scholars. These men were sources of information to Idrisi, adding to his own learning and knowledge gained in travel.

[Roger] had always taken a keen interest in reports from distant lands, and had questioned travellers and collected their stories. Idrisi was to collaborate with him, and was commissioned to compile a book containing all available data on the latitude and longitude of towns, the distances between them and their distribution in climatic zones. Reliable agents, accompanied by draughtsmen, were sent into various countries to collect information, on the basis of which the book and, later, the map [w]ere put together; this work took 15 years. The map was in the form of a silver tablet, probably measuring 3.5 x 1.5 metres; later, in 1160, this tablet fell into the hands of the mob and was smashed to pieces. In 1154, a few weeks before Roger's death, manuscripts of the book in Latin and Arabic were completed, together with the map, which was drawn on 70 sheets, and a small circular world map. Roger named the book *Nazhat al-Mushtak*, but the author named it *Kitab Rudjar*, i.e. "The Book of Roger," and the map "Tabula Rogeriana."

According to Arab sources, Idrisi composed a more detailed text and map in 1161 for Roger's son William II. While the first book was called (ostensibly by Idrisi himself) "The Amusement of him who desires to traverse the Earth," the second bore the title "The Gardens of Humanity and the Amusement of the Soul." Although this second work is not extant, a shortened version with the title "Garden of Joys" (1192), has survived; this consists of 73 maps in the form of an atlas, and is now known as the "Little Idrisi." Manuscripts of this version are preserved in various libraries: in Paris (2), Oxford (2), Leningrad, Constantinople and Cairo. There is a substantial difference between the two versions of 1154 and 1192. The later map is smaller and contains fewer names.[19]

Idrisi's view of the sea beyond Britain was a familiar one to the classical world, dark and impossible to penetrate to any distance

[19] Bagrow, *History of Cartography*, 28–56.

northward.[20] This is revealed in his account of the voyage of the Magurin brothers, which Beazley felt was somehow related to the Brendan tradition. In the twelfth century these Moslem brothers reputedly sailed westward to ascertain the oceanic limits. They found largely the same phenomena that the Carthaginians had reported a millenium and a half earlier—darkness, shoals, and the thick waves of a curdled sea.[21]

A case for more successful Arab ventures into the Atlantic has recently been made, using Chinese sources, by Hui-Lin Li, who concluded that contact between the east and west banks of the Atlantic was deliberate and long-range, as opposed to accidental, and that the peculiar products of native American agriculture and zoology were known, via the Arabs, across the South Atlantic and as far afield as China long before Columbus. The time span under consideration by Hui-Lin Li extends from the eleventh to the thirteenth centuries.[22]

The article by Hui-Lin Li leads into several other areas of scholarly controversy which must, at the least, be mentioned. One concerns the knowledge of maize in the Old World prior to the voyages of Columbus. Traces of maize or knowledge thereof in Northern Europe have proved rather illusive. The plant which Ailbe reportedly brought back from his transatlantic venture is certainly intriguing. Gislebertus of Autun depicted something which looks like maize in the sculpture of that venerable cathedral. Frederick J. Pohl has suggested that the "self-sown" grain of the Norse sagas is really "new sown," and that the "new" can be interpreted as unfamiliar—hence, a new kind of grain, obviously maize.[23]

Regarding maize in the north, one is tempted to remark that the fields are not barren but the pickings are slight. Theories and proffered proofs grow more luxuriantly further south, and literature concerning the pre-Columbian interchange of maize and many

---

[20] Carson, *The Sea Around Us*, 207–208.

[21] *Ibid.* See also Ashe, *Land to the West*, 138–39.

[22] Hui-Lin Li, "Mu-Lan-Pi: A Case for Pre-Columbian Transatlantic Travel by Arab Ships," *Harvard Journal of Asiatic Studies*, XXIII (1961), 114–26.

[23] Pohl, *Atlantic Crossings*, 140–41.

other crop plants between Africa and South America is rather extensive.[24]

The Arabs had southern neighbors, and these were reputed to have found the Atlantic no obstacle. The pre-Columbian contact of Negro Africa with America also has much documentation, although it currently appears as if much or most of such contact, although it may have pre-dated Columbus, came after A.D. 1250. Columbus himself is said to have referred to "canoes . . . which start from the coast of Guinea and navigate to the west with merchandise." [25]

Since the problem, at least for the moment, is only tangential to our own, let us rest the case with portions of Leo Wiener's summation:

> There are several foci from which the Negro traders spread in the two Americas. The eastern part of South America, where the Caraibs are mentioned, seems to have been reached by them from the West Indies. Another stream, possibly from the same focus, radiated to the north along roads marked by the presence of mounds, and reached as far as Canada. The chief cultural influence was exerted by a Negro colony in Mexico, most likely from Teotihuacan and Tuxtla, who may have been instrumental in establishing the city of Mexico. From here their influence pervaded the neighboring tribes, and ultimately, directly or indirectly, reached Peru.
>
> . . . . . .
>
> That the Negro civilization was carried chiefly by the trader is proved not only by Columbus' specific reference, but also by the presence of the African merchant, the *tangoman*, as *tiangizman* in Mexico, hence Aztec *tiangiz* "market," and by the universality of the blue and white shell-money from Canada to La Plata, and the use of shells as a coin in the Peru–Guatemala trade. The exceptional position of the merchants in Mexico, with the chief worships directly attributed to them,

[24] For a sampling, cf. the note on maize in *The Inter-American*, XII (November, 1965), presumably by the editor Carl B. Compton; G. F. Carter, "Archaeological Maize in West Africa," *Man*, XCV (May, 1964), 85–86; M. D. W. Jeffreys, "Maize and the Ambiguity in Columbus' Letter," *Anthropological Journal of Canada*, III (1965) 2–11; Leo Wiener, *Africa and the Discovery of America* (Philadelphia; 1920–22), *passim*.

[25] Wiener, *Africa and America*, II, 116, citing J. B. Thatcher, *Christopher Columbus* (New York, 1903), II, 379.

similarly testifies to the importance of the trader in the pre-Columbian, Africa—America relations.

. . . . . .

The African penetration in religion and civic life and customs was thorough and, to judge from the survival of the Arabic words in a Malinke or Soninke form in America, especially among the Caraibs and Aztecs, proceeded almost exclusively from the Mandingos, either the ancestors of the present Malinkes, or a tribe in which the Soninke language had not yet completely separated from its Malinke affinities.[26]

Although Europeans had not yet evidenced much interest in Africa, they were showing an increasing fascination with the exotic and the far away. One group of romances growing in popularity centered around Alexander the Great. In some of these, Alexander's visit to the bottom of the sea was elaborated upon. Most of the marvels witnessed by Alexander during his submarine visit, he considered too far beyond belief to report. He did point out, however, that beneath the sea the big fish ate the little ones.[27]

[26] Wiener, *Africa and America*, III, 365–66.
[27] *Li Romans d'Alixandre*, ed. Heinrich Michelant (Stuttgart, 1846), 259–62.

xv *Ebb and Flow*

GERVASE of Tilbury (c. 1211) wrote a book which placed him in the ranks of the geographers. This work, written for the Holy Roman Emperor Otto IV, was commonly called the *Otia Imperialia*, although it has also appeared under other titles.[1] Gervase's geographical sources were primarily Orosius, Isidore, and the *De Imagine Mundi*. His contributions were two: he attempted to prove conclusively what the literal interpreters of Scripture had long held to be true, that Jerusalem was the exact center of the world;[2] and, secondly, he was so impressed by the salt-making activity of the sun in the equatorial zone that he concluded it would be impossible to circumnavigate the *orbis terrae*, not only because of the frozen sea in the north but because the equatorial ocean would be too thick with salt to sail through.[3] Gervase, however, may have had more to contribute geographically than prose. He may well have been responsible for the Ebstorf map, formerly thought to date from later in the century. It illustrates his points and may originally have accompanied his manuscript.[4]

By the thirteenth century many of the older medieval texts and encyclopaedias were being forced to share table, desk, and shelf with handbooks and encyclopaedias of more recent vintage. The star of Martianus Capella, for example, was declining;[5] that of Bartholomaeus Anglicus was rising. Bartholomaeus (c. 1190–

[1] For example, *Liber de Mirabilibus Mundi*, or *Descriptio Totius Orbis.* Cf. Sarton, *Introduction to the History of Science*, II, 637.

[2] Cf. Wright, *Geographical Lore*, 259.

[3] *Otia Imperialia*, III, 40: "Hinc enim frigore congelatum sub septentrione, fit rigidum: illinc nimio solis ardore spisatum, transeuntibus efficitur ab Euro ad Austrum et meridiem immeabile." Cited in Kimble, *Geography in the Middle Ages*, 168.

[4] Bagrow, *History of Cartography*, 48–49.

[5] Stahl, "To a Better Understanding of Martianus Capella," 111–12.

1250), whose Englishness was of birth rather than residence, studied in Paris and lived thereafter on the continent. Some time around 1240 he wrote an encyclopaedic compilation for the "simple and the rude" entitled *De Proprietatibus Rerum*. This work contained a section devoted to physical geography and another devoted to political and economic geography (Books XIV and XV). The volume's popularity, which appears deserved, is indicated by many translations and early printed editions.[6]

Bartholomaeus' work was extremely long, comprehensive, uneven, and admirably organized. It was equally inclusive whether dealing with what he knew well or that which he knew least. The information he offered on the Atlantic Ocean was comfortably behind the times.[7] Bartholomaeus discussed England, the "most island of Ocean," Ireland, Scotia, Thanet, Finland, bordering on the ocean to the east of Norway, and Iceland, the last region in Europe in the north beyond Norway. Nothing in the passage indicates that Bartholomaeus realized that Iceland was an island.[8]

Between 1245 and 1250, the *De Imagine Mundi* was recast (not directly translated) into French. As *L'Image du Monde*, it maintained its popularity into modern times.[9] Subsequent translations were made from the popular French version into Hebrew, Yiddish, and English. Caxton presented an English version to the world in 1480.

Readers of *L'Image du Monde* were informed that the earth was a sphere but an extremely small one in comparison with the universe. Only one quarter of the earth was inhabited. The inhabited quarter, of course, contained Europe, Asia, Africa, and some islands in the sea. The islands discussed included Plato's Atlantis, the "lost island" which was found by St. Brendan ("& who that wil knowe it maye visyte his legende & rede it.");

[6] Cf. Robert Steele, *Mediaeval Lore from Bartholomew Anglicus* (London, 1924), 1.

[7] Cf. Maurice de Gandillac, "Encyclopédies Pre-Médiévales et Médiévales," *Journal of World History*, IX (1966), 516–17; Pierre Michaud-Quantin, "Petites Encyclopédies du XIIIᵉ Siècle," *Journal of World History*, IX (1966), 584–88.

[8] Steele, *Medieval Lore from Bartholomew Anglicus*, 84–87, 96–101.

[9] For the question of authorship see the introduction to William Caxton's *Mirrour of the World* (London, 1913), ix–xi.

Islonde, where day and night each lasted six months; and another island, near Ireland, where no man might die.[10]

The sea itself, the reader learned, ran around, by, and through the earth. In running through, it became pure, lost its salt, and appeared on the earth's surface to begin its rounds again. The sea was salt because in some places the sun beat upon it so intensely that it became agitated and stirred up the earth in the valleys of bitterness beneath it. This earth "medlyd" with the sea water made it salt.[11]

A Dominican, Vincent of Beauvais, compiled an encyclopedia, the *Speculum Maius*, around 1250. It was actually a vast collection of excerpts and material found in earlier works with little attempt at integration. In the *Speculum Naturale* the discussion of the ocean in general consisted of citations from Aristotle, Isidore, *De Imagine Mundi*, Adelard, and Macrobius.[12]

In the thirty-second book of the *Speculum Naturale*, after discussing the regions of Asia, Europe, and Africa, Vincent turned to the islands "in the ocean which girds the earth." This section was based almost exclusively on Solinus and Isidore. He treated Britain, Thanatos, Thule, the Orcades, Scotia, and Hibernia in traditional fashion. After the usual phrases in regard to Thule, however, he added without comment a quotation from Solinus which referred to "Thyle," an Indian island upon which the trees never lost their leaves.[13] Continuing around the girdle of the earth, he wrote of the Fortunate Isles, the Gorgades, the Hesperides, and the Indian islands including "Tyle."

Vincent is singled out by Taylor and Richey in their book *The Geometrical Seaman* for his mention of the compass:

A Dominican, Vincent of Beauvais, writing about 1250, also describes

[10] *Ibid.*, 51–56, 59–61, 66–67, 94, 96, 98. Atlantis is not referred to by name. Plato's testimony is given as to size, but the island is said to have been destroyed since the time of Plato. Re the death-free island, cf. Cambrensis, *Topographia Hibernica*, II, 4. He reports two islands in a lake in Munster—on one no one can die; on the other no female can live.

[11] *Ibid.*, 109, 115.

[12] Vincent of Beauvais, *Speculum Naturale*, V, 13–14 (Venetijs, 1494).

[13] *Ibid.*, XXXII, 16–17. That his method was frequently more mechanical than inspired is revealed by the fact that he includes in this citation the lines which follow in Solinus and refer to the Caucasus mountains.

how when clouds prevent sailors from seeing sun or star they rub the point of a needle on the magnet stone; they then transfix it through a straw and float it in a basin of water. The lodestone, he says, is then moved round the basin faster and faster pursued by the needle and then suddenly snatched away. The needle stops dead and remains pointed towards the *Stella Maris*, that is to say the Pole Star. The idea that the needle pointed towards the star which had guided seamen for so long is natural enough, and was doubtless the more attractive for its ancient association with Our Lady, Star of the Sea.[14]

Albertus Magnus, to whom history has given a surname not often applied to scholars, and who has been referred to as "the only saint who, with all regard for twentieth-century notions, can justly be termed a scientist,[15] was credited by Beazley with a mention of Vinland,[16] a citation this investigator has been unable to justify. Nevertheless, this fellow Dominican and contemporary of Vincent of Beauvais warrants mention because he felt reason demanded that the southern temperate zone be inhabited.[17]

The writings of Roger Bacon date from the latter half of the thirteenth century; therefore, he was at least a near contemporary of Vincent. His work included some of the earliest research on the polar properties of the magnet. He counseled that the inhabited world stretched over much more than half the world's circumference and that India was closer to Europe on the west than on the east. To defend his thesis, he summoned many of the witnesses from whom we heard much earlier in the course of our own investigation:

Ptolemy . . . in the *Almagest* . . . states that habitation is not known except in a quarter of the earth, namely, in that in which we dwell. . . . But Aristotle maintains . . . that more than a fourth is inhabited. . . . Aristotle says that the sea is small between the end of Spain on the west and the beginning of India on the east. Seneca . . . says that this sea is navigable in a few days if the wind is favorable.[18]

[14] Taylor and Richey, *The Geometrical Seaman*, 5–6.
[15] Albertus Magnus, *Libellus de Alchimia* (Berkeley, 1958), xv–xvi.
[16] Beazley, *Dawn of Modern Geography*.
[17] Cited in Kimble, *Geography in the Middle Ages*, 84.
[18] This passage from Bacon's *Opus Majus* is cited more extensively in Kimble, *Geography in the Middle Ages*, 86–87. The reference to Averroes is another indication of Western Europe's debt to the Arab world in science during the later Middle Ages. This is also true of the reference to

Bacon was interested in the ocean and recommended that underseas exploration be undertaken.[19] He also pressed for an accurate and complete survey of the world, being aware that the maps of his time left much to be desired.[20]

Bacon himself designed a map to accompany his unheeded recommendations for a world survey; the map unfortunately has been lost. Others of less promise have survived. The Psalter Map, (c. 1225), four inches in diameter and crowded with legends, was included in a manuscript of the *Book of Psalms*. It depicted a world-circle with Jerusalem placed in the exact center. Beazley aptly commented that the Psalter Map "shows us 'World Knowledge' removed as far as possible from the comparative science of the Ancient Imperial World, and yet quite untouched by the new light of the later Middle Ages." [21] The 1250 map of Matthew of Paris and the famous Hereford map, which dates from the late thirteenth century, did not reveal any notable advances in geographical knowledge.

Happily, the people whose need for accurate mapping was the most apparent were developing maps, or sailing charts, of their own. These were the portolano charts discussed earlier, which sailors relied on in the Age of Discovery. The development of such charts followed almost inevitably the introduction of the compass, and there were undoubtedly many in use by 1250.[22] The course was set and the way was west.

Ptolemy's *Almagest*. The Arabic title given this work reveals that it was preserved and reintroduced to the west by the Arabs. Bacon's arguments were repeated by Pierre d'Ailly (1350–1420) in his *Imago Mundi* and through this work were known to Columbus.

[19] De Latil and Rivoire, *Man and the Underwater World*, 88.

[20] Sarton, *Introduction to History of Science*, II, 958; Beazley, *Dawn of Modern Geography*, III, 504–505.

[21] Beazley, *Dawn of Modern Geography*, II, 618. For dating see Bagrow, *History of Cartography*, 45.

[22] Cf. Kimble, *Geography in the Middle Ages*, 189–90; Sarton, *Introduction to the History of Science*, II, 1047–49.

XVI *The Sea Around Them: A Summary*

Surveying the material available to the thirteenth-century investigator of the Atlantic Ocean, it would seem that, if he weighed his authorities carefully and supplemented what they had to say with his own reasoning, he would have probably concluded that the earth was a sphere and that the ocean also conformed and had a spherical surface. This, though, is only a probability. If he concluded otherwise, he would have been in the company of a vast array of people who also rejected sphericity. Those who supported an alternative, however, were in frequent disagreement among themselves.

The sphericity of the earth, a concept advanced by the savants of antiquity and preserved for the Middle Ages by authorities such as Capella and Macrobius, was widely accepted in the thirteenth century. Bede had supported this concept, and it had eventually been maintained by a diverse group of scholars. Adam of Bremen and the author of the *King's Mirror* supported it in the north, the author of *De Imagine Mundi* in the south. Through *L'Image du Monde*, a popularization of the latter work, it received great currency. Abelard had accepted the concept of a spherical earth a century before, but had denied the spherical surface of the ocean itself which he felt was not earth-contained. His spherical earth floated half submerged in a great ocean sea—this apparently had been his reasoned compromise between sphericity and the beliefs of many of his colleagues.

Twelve hundred years earlier, the elder Pliny had commented on the mighty battle in progress between the learned and the "common herd" concerning the shape of the earth. The idea that the earth was a sphere was especially subject to attack because it implied the possibility of human life in "inaccessible" areas. A compromise such as Abelard's apparently had not been suggested. Sphericity was also attacked because of the implication that people somewhere walked with their feet toward the center of the earth and their bodies upside down.

From antiquity on, many were vague or unconcerned about the overall shape of the earth. Some paid lip service to a spherical world and proceeded to describe or construct systems in which sphericity played no necessary part. Some avoided the problem by concerning themselves with the "inhabited earth" or "known world." The "known" inhabited land mass was known with imprecision. It might be represented as square, oblong, circular, or approximating any of the haphazard postures of the amorphous amoeba. With the establishment of Christianity, many concepts from the fringes of early Greek science—concepts which had nearly succumbed during the classical period—came again to the fore with new champions who were found not among the "common herd" but among the intellectual leadership. The oblong land mass based by Dionysius Periegetes upon old Greek sources was to find frequent support among Christians. The rectangular world of Ephorus would receive the stamp of approval from Cosmas, who had resolved that he himself should be the model for Christian geographers.

Haunted by the ghosts of the corollaric antipodes, the Christian apologist Lactantius attacked the concept of a spherical earth with considered vehemence and sarcasm. St. Basil, on the other hand, refused to be concerned, reminding his listeners gently that, since the great Moses had been silent as to the earth's shape, this knowledge was not necessary to salvation and the search for such was vanity. St. Augustine, also noncommittal as to the shape of the earth, was quite firm on the point that, with the exception of a few islands which men might reach in ships from the inhabited land mass, the earth was not otherwise peopled. Augustine and the Church Fathers were convinced that natural barriers existed sufficient to prevent contact between the inhabited world and any other land masses which might exist. Since people living upon such land masses, according to this reasoning, would neither be descendants of Adam nor able to receive the message of Christ, belief in their existence was heresy.

Heresy, however, seemed no concern of Martianus Capella, nor of Macrobius. These pagan-minded authors produced textbooks of secular knowledge which the school masters of early medieval Europe depended upon and preserved, in spite of the fact that antipodal inhabited continents were found upon the surface of the spherical world depicted therein. The doctrine of sphere and antipodes advanced in their pages was frequently, in whole or in part, challenged, ignored, or misinterpreted. This misinterpretation is nowhere more apparent than in the work of Isidore of Seville and his moralizing copyist, Raban Maur. Their world, although they used terminology of classical science, was a flat circular disc surrounded by ocean; the antipodes only dwelt "according to story" in an unknown region to the south. Bede and others who clung to the idea of a spherical earth found a way to sidestep the charge of heresy by distinguishing between an inhabited zone in the northern hemisphere and a "habitable" zone in the southern hemisphere.

In the ninth century, John Scot Erigena, preparing a commentary on Capella, indicated his acceptance of inhabited antipodal continents, but a later work revealed that he reconsidered. An eleventh-century tract, written by Manegold of Lauenbach and directed against a contemporary with Macrobian views, showed that such a doctrine was still being accepted and rejected. Two centuries later, however, Albertus Magnus, Dominican doctor, member of an order created to combat heretical opinion, and mentor of Thomas Aquinas, aroused little opposition when he asserted that reason demanded the existence of an inhabited temperate zone in the southern hemisphere. Two centuries later, the Age of Discovery would reveal that there really had not been any problem to begin with. Actually the man with the book was the last to realize this. While Gervase of Tilbury was busily proving that Jerusalem was the exact center of the earth and that the Bible literally interpreted revealed a true picture of the world, while maps of the T-O type were growing in monastic popularity (except among those whom Hugo of St. Victor had convinced that the world was to be constructed using the shape of Noah's ark as a basis), seamen with the aid of the newly introduced compass were evolving practical sailing charts.

In the North Atlantic, where for centuries Irish monks had persisted in sailing westward in search of the eastern earthly Paradise and island hermitages, the Norse had long since settled upon Ultima Thule and had, without realizing it, already landed upon an antipodal continent. Even among them, traditional learning was so strong that, although their world picture differed considerably from that of their southern brethren, its overall aspects remained strikingly close to that of Isidore.

The thirteenth-century investigator would have found the salinity of the sea variously explained. Everyone, however, was generally agreed that the heat of the sun had something to do with it. The majority felt that the process whereby the sun made the sea salt was limited to, or most extensive in, the equatorial region. Few, however, carried this idea to the extreme of Gervase of Tilbury who conceived of an equatorial ocean so thickened with salt as to make it unnavigable.

Those who felt that the ocean was made bitter in the equatorial zone explained that currents emanating from this region carried the salinity to the remaining gulfs and seas. This theory conformed basically to the Macrobian explanation of oceanic currents. The theory advanced by Aristotle that oceanic currents flowed from north to south because regions in the north were higher had several apparent weaknesses. Macrobius on the other hand provided an explanation which allowed continual movement in diverse directions. Furthermore his currents originating in equatorial waters, flowing east and west, then bifurcating and flowing north and south, were reported to cause, by the violence of their meeting in the polar regions, the ebb and flow of ocean. In the eleventh century, Adelard of Bath attempted to blend the two explanations. He had the northbound Macrobian currents failing to meet because interposing Aristotelian elevations prevented the collision. But the elevations served somewhat the same purpose by causing a backwash. The Macrobian explanation had other rivals. There were more than a few whose explanation was supremely simple—the ocean was an agent of God and moved anywhere and everywhere at His direction. There were others who thought that oceanic currents were caused by an abyss or series of abysses into which oceanic waters were sucked and then spewed out again. The abyss, of course, would also serve as explanation for tides.

The phenomenon of the tides had challenged the explicative ingenuity of men through the ages. Some people recognized very early that the moon had an effect upon the ocean. Pytheas of Massilia was a champion of the view that the oceanic tides were the result of lunar influence. Pliny the Elder, whose authority was acknowledged in the Middle Ages, gave such lunar influence his full support. St. Basil, St. Augustine, St. Ambrose, and other Christian teachers accepted it. St. Basil explained that respiration of the moon pulled the surface of the sea toward it and its expiration pushed the waters back. The Venerable Bede not only recognized the lunar effect upon the tides but demonstrated their predictability. Yet, with all this support, the idea of the moon's influence upon the ocean actually lost ground during the medieval period.

Orosius, the protegé of St. Augustine, said nothing about the moon's effect upon tides but he explained the difference between spring and neap tides as the result of internal loss of water and natural absorption. Macrobius knew that tidal phenomenon was concurrent with phases of the moon but felt that these were both in some mysterious way influenced by the number seven. Isidore of Seville had no need of the moon in his explanation of the tides; winds caused them. The most successful rival of the lunar explanation was the "abysmal" explanation of Paul the Deacon who wrote during the latter half of the eighth century. Isidore of Seville had given an account of the *Abyssus* which was the "impenetrable deep of the waters," but this abyss, except for supplying water, had no effect upon the ocean's behavior. Paul the Deacon, perhaps influenced by Germanic tradition, was to add considerably to this concept. He reported whirlpools in the ocean which twice each day sucked in the surface waters of the ocean and spewed them forth again. These whirlpools were thereafter associated with the abyss and became a very popular explanation of the tides. Adam of Bremen, although familiar with the works of Bede which discussed the lunar influence upon tides, explained tides as the result of the action of the abyss. The author of the *De Imagine Mundi* devoted a chapter to the lunar explanation, but followed it, just in case, with a chapter which confirmed that the tides were caused by the sucking and spewing of the abyss. The English scholar Alexander Neckam, an older contemporary of our hypothetical thirteenth-century investigator, concluded that the tides presented a vexing problem that was without solution. In the same period, however, Giraldus Cambrensis and others had no doubt as to the moon's responsibility.

God had commanded the water of the earth to be gathered into one place. The logical candidate for this one place was the ocean, which was itself frequently considered to be the abyss. Christian scholars found support for this view in classical scholarship. Homer had indicated that the ocean deep was the source of all rivers, springs, and seas. The elder Pliny explained that veins in the earth carried the oceanic waters underground until they appeared again, purified by their progress through the earth, as rivers and springs which made their way once more toward the sea. This cycle became a standard explanation for the fact that, although the ocean was continually being fed by rivers and streams, it did not overflow. Sometimes, of course, there were additional reasons—perhaps the bitter oceanic waters consumed the fresh water; or perhaps the sun, or clouds, or winds drew water from the ocean's surface. But Alexander Neckam, who died in 1230, offered an alternative explanation; the ocean was not the source but the grave of all waters and its level was continually rising. In fact, the ocean was already "visibly" higher than the land and but for the will of God would overflow it.

The Mediterranean savant had painted a somber picture of the Atlantic, a shallow sea abounding in mud shoals where, not far from the pillars of Hercules, the winds failed and the sea became sluggish. There were many mariners in the Atlantic who knew better, but they were the last to write about it; and many of the Mediterranean concepts persisted, especially in the mind of the scholar.

The ocean itself was said to forbid inquiry. Seaweed and sea monsters were apt to stay the progress of a ship, and the seamen who did manage to penetrate far to west or north would find nothing but perpetual fog and darkness. As knowledge increased, the areas of horror and mystery diminished in size or were pushed farther toward the periphery.

In many ways exploration seaward was considered to border on sacrilege. Tacitus had indicated that it was "more religious and more reverent to believe in the works of Deity than to comprehend them," and Horace spoke of "godless ships bound madly in contempt o'er channels not allowed." The men of Germanicus, when at sea in the north, had this same attitude: "The gods call us back and they forbid mortal eyes to see the boundary of things. Why do we violate strange seas and sacred waters with our oars?" They expected that at any moment the wind would fail, the ship would stick fast in sludge, and sea monsters would mangle and devour them.

Tacitus reported that just to the north of Britain the sea was sluggish and heavy. Aristotle taught that the Atlanic was "shallow owing to the mud." Earlier, Plato had explained the mud as being caused by the subsidence of Atlantis. He may not have intended this explanation to be taken literally, but it persisted. The *De Imagine Mundi* reported Plato's island which sank beneath the waves had curdled the sea in the vicinity.

The idea that the entire Atlantic was shallow could not continue to be held. The Irish Dicuil would challenge the classical Mediterranean dictum that this sea was deeper than the Atlantic and ask who had done the measuring. Many obstacles to Atlantic navigation had been suggested in classical times. The Carthaginians had reported, in an apparent attempt to deceive competitors, that a few days' sail westward into the Atlantic brought one to a region of seaweed-covered reefs which were exposed at low tide. A similar account, perhaps from the same source, was found in the *Periplus* of Scylax. He told of a great system of rocky reefs not far out in the Atlantic which stretched from Europe to Africa. This idea was soon dispelled as seamen sailed with greater and greater frequency over the area where the reefs were reported to exist.

Any such obstacles, if they existed, had to be farther away. Proserpine, under Claudian's direction, placed "Ocean's glassy shallows" at the farthest edge.[1] Plutarch also placed a muddy shallow sea which was difficult to sail through on the outer fringe of ocean. He accounted for this sludge not by the sinking of Atlantis but thought it the result of alluvial deposit from the many streams flowing into the ocean from the great continent which formed the ocean's other side. This, he added, made the sea "heavy like land,

---

[1] Claudian, *Rape of Proserpine*, 246–70.

whence the opinion prevailed that it was actually frozen." From
the time of Pytheas it had been repeated that the frozen sea was one
day's sail beyond Thule. Similar statements appeared again and
again. Dicuil reported that Irish monks had verified the fact, and
well they may have.

The hardy Scandinavians demonstrated the possibility of living
and sailing in the frozen north. But Scandinavians also had their
respect for tradition. Adam of Bremen was assured by the Danish
king that the gloomy region of ice and perpetual mist began just
beyond Vinland. The Scandinavians, as they advanced across the
Atlantic, expected to find Ginnungagap, the great gulf of the abyss,
in the area just beyond. At first it was located near Iceland, then
near Greenland, then near Vinland; and at last, to preserve the idea
of the existence of the abyss somewhere, they were forced to re-
duce Ginnungagap to a strait which joined a Mediterranean Atlantic to an "outer ocean sea." Farther south, Gervase of Tilbury
added to the congealed frozen sea in the north one in the torrid
zone congealed with salt, although natives to the south were not
aware of this congestion.

Congealed seas would have made circumnavigation of the "known
world" impossible, but scattered here and there in the works of
Pliny, Mela, Solinus, and Capella, the thirteenth-century reader
could find reports of real or supposed circumnavigations of Europe,
Asia, and Africa. These reports must have served to cast flickering
doubts upon statements which indicated the impossibility of such a
feat.

In discussions of the Atlantic to westward, there was an abundance of material concerned in one way or another with death.
This was scarcely strange. The region of the setting sun was in
many mythologies connected with the end of life. Egyptians had
"gone west" long before Hiawatha, and the Greeks had placed their
Islands of the Blest in the Western Ocean.

The island of Thanet, off the northeast coast of Kent, early in the
Middle Ages lent its name to an equation with *Thanatos*, the Greek
word for "death." The poet Claudian wrote that one standing on
the furthermost western shores of Gaul might hear weeping and
see the shades of the dead as they went by. Lactantius confirmed

that the Atlantic was the sea of darkness and death, and he felt that spirits passing that way had reason for weeping. It was the devil's territory. Lactantius reported that the "west is ascribed to that disturbed and depraved mind, because it conceals the light, because it makes men die and perish for their sins." The Byzantine historian Procopius told of an island named Brittia which was divided by a wall like Britain's, and, he reported, the region west of the wall was the abode of death. To this place the souls of the dead were borne from the continent through the good offices of the coastal fishermen. All of this made the abode of death at first too close for comfort and then too close for belief. It too was forced to go west.

The association of the Western Ocean with death did not necessarily imply an association exclusively with the damned, although the sober and judicious author of the *King's Mirror* explained that the volcanoes of Iceland were vents from Hell itself. The Greek Islands of the Blest, where dead heroes had been rewarded with the pleasantest of surroundings, persisted in names or in the characteristics of the Fortunate Islands, the Islands of the Gods, the Hesperides, and Avalon. The thirteenth-century reader might find in Geoffrey of Monmouth's *Vita Merlini* an account of the "island of apples which men call the Fortunate Isle" to which the wounded King Arthur was borne. He might have found, in a manuscript dealing with St. Brendan, an account of the monastic family of St. Ailbe that awaited Judgment Day on an island in the Atlantic. He might have realized the implication of Brendan's seeking the eastern earthly Paradise in the Western Ocean, or of Snedgus and Mac-Riagla finding in the west an island upon which Enoch and Elijah were living.

In the *Vita Merlini*, the thirteenth-century investigator would have found Hell placed in the south surrounded by the burning equatorial ocean, directly contradicting the location for Hell suggested by the *King's Mirror*. In the works of Hugo of St. Victor there was support for the northern Hell and, moreover, confirming evidence that men might very well be awaiting Doomsday on Atlantic islands. Hugo believed that the place of universal resurrection was somewhere in the Atlantic, and that the day was very near. After the last judgment, the elect would make their way southward, the damned to Hell in the north.

When Phoenicians or Carthaginians had discovered islands in the Atlantic, these were equated by the Greeks with the Islands of the Blest. Sertorius, in Spain, was reported to have met sailors who described these fortunate islands in glowing terms. Isidore averred that the Fortunate Islands were so fertile that in an earlier day they had been mistakenly reputed to be Paradise. Claudian referred to the "common verdure of those gardens of the Hesperides which story had clothed with gold." Familiarity bred disillusionment. Islands abounding in marvels would have to be sought farther out in the sea. There they could continue to exist with wonders equal to, or identical with, those attributed earlier to islands much nearer the European seaboard.

Many Irish mariners, most of them monastics, were reported to have landed upon marvelous islands. Others sought, and some of them found, islands abounding not in golden apples but in silence as precious. The search for deserted islands as sites for hermitages had been going on long before the lights of history and Christianity had reached the greater Britannic scene. With the arrival of Christianity, this practice increased, as is amply evidenced in the pages of Adamnan's *Life of St. Columba*. The practice continued until the arrival of the Scandinavian Viking invaders. The Irish scholar Dicuil testified concerning the islands in the Atlantic north of Britain: "Upon some of these I have lived, others I have visited, yet others I have seen and of others I have read." He might have added "and of others I have heard," since in the same work he included material told him by monks who thirty years before had sojourned upon the island of Thule.

By Thule, Dicuil meant Iceland. The first man reported to have visited Thule was the Greek savant Pytheas of Massilia. However, in the centuries that followed, many people were not quite sure where Pytheas had found Thule, and it was variously placed to the west, northwest, north, or northeast of Britain. This is not particularly strange considering the fact that Adam of Bremen could place Greenland, of which he had firsthand information, to the northeast of Europe. Furthermore there were frequent attempts to equate Thule with places which an author knew existed. Tacitus seems to have thought that Thule was in the Shetlands; others thought it to be Norway. Some, of course, thought that Pytheas had made the whole thing up. Nearly everyone, however, agreed that Thule was the "ultimate" land and that it was to be found on the outermost edge of the inhabitable world. Seneca had predicted that the day would come when Thule would no longer be the limit of the lands, and by the thirteenth century this had come to pass. Since the time of Dicuil, there had been general agreement that Ultima Thule was Iceland, and by the thirteenth century Iceland, and Greenland beyond it, had long been settled.

Prior to Dicuil's account, Ultima Thule was usually located somewhere in the northern ocean, for the most part to the north or northwest of Britain. In the middle of the sixth century, however, Jordanes had placed Thule at the farthest edge of the ocean toward the west. A century later, an unknown Ravennese geographer, perhaps because of discrepancies in his sources, reported two Thules in the Atlantic—one near Britain and the other off the coast of Spain. If the investigator had examined the twelfth-century map of Lambert of St. Omer he would have found an island named Thule in the Atlantic off Gibraltar. The Welsh Giraldus was well aware of Iceland but did not know where the island could be which was referred to as Thule in the works of Solinus, Orosius, Isidore, and other authors. No one in his part of the country, he reported, had ever heard of it. The wonder-filled Thule could not settle down to be historic Iceland. Furthermore it was becoming increasingly confused with an "Indian" island.

Seneca had pronounced long before that India was not many days' sail westward from Spain. A few years after 1250, Roger Bacon would marshal authority in support of his opinion that India was nearer Europe on the west than on the east. This could not be accepted by those who held the concept, developing in the farthest north, that armlike extensions of Europe and Africa made an almost landlocked sea of the Atlantic. However, there were those to the south who were aware of this northern concept but nevertheless knew that Scandinavian seamen had found not only an Iceland but a "Wineland" in the Atlantic. Those who believed that the earth was a sphere would have little difficulty imagining that this Wineland was on or off the coast of India. St. Brendan and other Irishmen had reportedly made similar discoveries. Brendan, moreover, had sought the terrestrial Paradise, usually located on or off the shores of eastern Asia, by sailing west. From time to time, Indians had been reported to have landed on European shores. These Indians were usually considered to have come via a Northeast Passage (a Vinland–Finland confusion might also figure in this), but the transatlantic possibility remained.

Our imaginary investigator probably reasoned that India, or some other large land area, lay across the Atlantic—whether an extension of Europe or Africa, an antipodal continent, or the great outer continent of Plato and Plutarch. Furthermore there were, he could be sure, "thrice fifty isles in the ocean to the west."

Far out in the Atlantic, on Greenland, there was already an outpost of possibly ten thousand Europeans, and inhabited land had been reported farther to the south and west. Armed with portolano charts, the compass, the astrolabe, and courage, more navigators would probe the Atlantic in the years which followed. Some of the seamen might ask themselves, as the Roman sailors of Germanicus had, "Are we seeking people located on the other side? Why do we violate strange seas and sacred waters?" The mystery and the fear were beginning to fade and the fog was beginning to lift. Ocean, for the most part, no longer forbade inquiry; it actually seemed to invite it.

Bibliography

I PRIMARY SOURCES AND SOURCE BOOKS

Abélard. *Expositio in Hexaemeron.* Vol. CLXXVIII of *Patrologiae Cursus Completus, Series Latina,* J. P. Migne (ed.). Paris, 1879.

Adam of Bremen. *Gesta Hammaburgensis Ecclesiae Pontificum.* Vol. CXLVI of *Patrologiae Cursus Completus, Series Latina,* J. P. Migne (ed.). Paris, 1884.

—————. *History of the Archbishops of Hamburg-Bremen.* Translated by F. J. Tschan. New York, 1959.

Adamnan. *Vita S. Columbae.* Edited and translated by J. T. Fowler. Oxford, 1894.

Adelard of Bath. *Quaestiones Naturales.* Edited by Martin Müller. Vol. XXXI of *Beiträge zur Geschichte der Philosophie und Theologie des Mittelalters* (1934).

Aelfric. *Exameron Anglice.* Edited and translated by S. J. Crawford. Hamburg, 1921.

Aelian. *De Natura Animalium.* London, 1744. 2 Vols.

—————. *Varia Historia.* London, 1701. 2 Vols.

Aethicus of Istria. *Die Kosmographie des Istrier Aithikos.* Edited by Heinrich Wuttke. Leipzig, 1853.

Albertus Magnus. *Libellus de Alchimia.* Berkeley, 1958.

Alfred. *Alfred the Great's Translation of Orosius.* Included in Pauli's *Life of Alfred the Great.* Translated by B. Thorpe. London, 1902.

—————. *King Alfred's Version of the Consolation of Boethius.* Translated by Walter J. Sedgefield. Oxford, 1940.

—————. *King Alfred's Orosius.* Edited by Henry Sweet (Old English text and Latin original). London, 1883.

Ambrose, St., Bishop of Milan. *Hexaemeron.* Vol. XIV of *Patrologiae Cursus Completus, Series Latina,* J. P. Migne (ed.). Paris, 1882.

Ammianus Marcellinus. *History.* Translated by John C. Rolfe. Cambridge, Mass., 1935. 3 Vols.

Anglo-Saxon Chronicle. Translated by E. E. C. Gomme. London, 1909.

Apollodorus. *The Library*. Translated by James G. Frazer. New York, 1921. 2 Vols.

Ari (Frode) Thorgilsson. *Islendingabok*. Vol. XX of *Islandica*. Ithaca, 1930.

―――. *Islendingabok*. Vol. XXIII of *Thule*. Baetke (ed.). Jena, 1928.

Aristotle. *De Caelo*. Translated by J. L. Stocks, Oxford, 1922.

―――. *Meteorologica*. Translated by E. W. Webster. Oxford, 1923.

Aristotle. (pseudo). *De Mirabilibus Auscultationibus*. Translated by L. D. Dowdall. Oxford, 1909.

―――. *De Mundo*. Translated by E. S. Forster. Oxford, 1914.

Arrian. *Anabasis of Alexander*. Translated by E. Iliff Robson. New York, 1933. 2 Vols.

Augustine (Aurelius Augustinus). *City of God*. Translated by Marcus Dods. New York, 1950.

―――. *Confessions*. Translated by Edward B. Pusey. New York, 1949.

Augustus. *Res Gestae Divi Augusti*. Edited by Jean Gagé. Paris, 1935.

Aulus Gellius, *Noctes Atticae*. New York, 1927.

Avienus. *Ora Maritima*. Edited by A. Berthelot. Paris, 1934.

Baetke, Walter (ed.). *Thule: Altnordische Dichtung und Prosa*. Jena, 1928. 24 Vols.

Basil. *Hexaemeron*. Translated by Bloomfield Jackson in Vol. VIII of *Select Library of Nicene and Post-Nicene Fathers of the Christian Church*. Second Series. New York, 1895.

Bede. *De Natura Rerum*. Vol. XC of *Patrologiae Cursus Completus, Series Latina*, J. P. Migne (ed.). Paris, 1862.

―――. *De Temporum Ratione*. Vol. XC of *Patrologiae Cursus Completus, Series Latina*, J. P. Migne (ed.). Paris, 1862.

Bede (pseudo). *De Mundi Coelestis Terrestrisque Constitutione*. Vol. XC of *Patrologiae Cursus Completus, Series Latina*, J. P. Migne (ed.). Paris, 1862.

Benoit. *Chronique des Ducs de Normandie*. Edited by Francisque Michel. Paris, 1836. 2 Vols.

Betha Coluimb Cille. Edited and translated by R. Henebry in Vol. V of *Zeitschrift für Celtische Philologie* (1905), 26–87.

Boethius. *Consolation of Philosophy*. Translated by "I. T." and H. F. Stewart. New York, 1918.

Caesar. *Commentary on Gallic War*. New York, 1917.

Capella (Martianus Capella). *De Nuptiis Philologiae et Mercurii*. Edited by F. Eyssenhardt. Leipzig, 1865.

Caxton, William. *Mirrour of the World*. London, 1913.

Cicero. *On the Commonwealth*. Translated by George H. Sabine and Stanley B. Smith. Columbus, Ohio, 1929.

Claudian. *Works*. Translated by Maurice Platnauer. New York, 1922. 2 Vols.

Cosmas Indicopleustes. *Christian Topography*. Translated by J. W. McCrindle. London, 1897.

De Imagine Mundi (ascribed to Honorius of Autun). Vol. CLXXII of *Patrologiae Cursus Completus, Series Latina*, J. P. Migne (ed.). Paris, 1895.

Dicuil. *Liber de Mensura Orbis Terrae*. Edited by G. Parthey. Berlin, 1870.

Dio Cassius. *Roman History*. Translated by Ernest Cary. New York, 1916. 9 Vols.

Diodorus Siculus. *Works*. Translated by C. H. Oldfather. Cambridge, Mass., 1935. 10 Vols.

Diogenes Laertius. *The Lives and Opinions of Eminent Philosophers*. Translated by C. D. Yonge. London, 1853.

Dionysius Periegetes. *Periegesis*. Edited by G. Bernhardy. Leipzig, 1828.

Florus (Lucius Annaeus Florus). *Epitome Rerum Romanorum*. Translated by E. S. Forster. New York, 1929.

Frederick II of Hohenstaufen. *The Art of Falconry*. Translated and edited by Casey A. Wood and F. Marjorie Fyfe. Stanford, 1961.

Geoffrey of Monmouth. *Historia Regum Britanniae*. Edited by Acton Griscom. New York, 1929.

————. *Vita Merlini*. Edited and translated by John Jay Perry. Vol. X of *University of Illinois Studies in Language and Literature*, (August, 1925), 3.

Giraldus Cambrensis. *Topographia Hibernica*. Edited by James F. Dimock. Vol. V of Giraldus Cambrensis, *Opera*. London, 1867.

Guiot de Provins. *La Bible*. In *Les Oeuvres de Guiot de Provins*. Edited by John Orr. Manchester, 1915.

Hakluyt, Richard. *Principal Navigations Voyages Traffiques & Discoveries of the English Nation*. New York, 1904. 12 Vols.

Hanno. *The Periplus of Hanno*. Translated by Wilfred H. Schoff. Philadelphia, 1912.

Hennig, Richard. *Terrae Incognitae*. Leiden, 1944–53. 3 Vols.

Hermannsson, Halldór. *The Vinland Sagas*. Edited with an Introduction, Variants and Notes. Vol. XXX of *Islandica*. Ithaca, 1944.

Herodotus. *History*. Translated by A. D. Godley. New York, 1920. 4 Vols.

Hesiod. *The Homeric Hymns and Homerica*. Translated by H. G. Eveleyn-White. New York, 1936.

Homer. *Iliad*. Translated by A. T. Murray. New York, 1925. 2 Vols.

————. *Odyssey*. Translated by A. T. Murray. New York, 1919. 2 Vols.

Horace. *Poems*. Translated by A. H. Bryce. London, 1907.

Hugo of St. Victor. *De Arca Noe Morali*. Vol. CLXXVI of *Patrologiae Cursus Completus, Series Latina*, J. P. Migne (ed.). Paris, 1879.

————. *De Arca Noe Mystica*. Vol. CLXXVI of *Patrologiae Cursus Completus, Series Latina*, J. P. Migne (ed.). Paris, 1879.

————. *De Sacramentis*. Vol. CLXXVI of *Patrologiae Cursus Completus, Series Latina*, J. P. Migne (ed.). Paris, 1879.

Hugo of St. Victor (pseudo). *Tractatus Exceptionum*. Vol. CLXXVII of *Patrologiae Cursus Completus, Series Latina*, J. P. Migne (ed.). Paris, 1879.

Hyginus. *Poeticon Astronomicon*. In Augustin van Staveren (ed.), *Auctores Mythographi Latini*. Amstelaed, 1742.

L'Image du Monde. See Caxton, William. *Mirrour of the World*.

Isidore. *De Natura Rerum*. Vol. LXXXIII of *Patrologiae Cursus Completus, Series Latina*, J. P. Migne (ed.). Paris, 1862.

————. *De Ordine Creaturarum*. Vol. LXXXIII of *Patrologiae Cursus Completus, Series Latina*, J. P. Migne (ed.). Paris, 1862.

————. *Etymologiae*. Edited by W. M. Lindsay. Oxford, 1911. 2 vols.

John Scot Erigena. *Annotationes in Marcianum*. Edited and translated by Cora E. Lutz. Cambridge, Mass., 1939.

————. *De Divisione Naturae*. Vol. CXXII of *Patrologiae Cursus Completus, Series Latina*, J. P. Migne (ed.). Paris, 1865.

Jones, Charles W. (ed.). *Bedae Opera de Temporibus*. Cambridge, Mass., 1943.

Jordanes. *Getica*. Vol. V of *M. G. H.*, *Auctores Antiquissimi*, Theodor Mommsen (ed.). Berlin, 1882.

————. *The Origin and Deeds of the Goths*. Translated by Charles C. Mierow. Princeton, 1908.

The King's Mirror. Translated by L. M. Larson. New York, 1917.

Lactantius. *Divine Institutions*. Translated by William Fletcher. Vol. XXI of *Ante-Nicene Christian Library*, Alexander Roberts and James Donaldson (eds.). Edinburgh, 1871.

Lambert of St. Omer. *Liber Floridus* (Notitia et Excerpta). Vol. CLXIII of *Patrologiae Cursus Completus, Series Latina*, J. P. Migne (ed.). Paris, 1893.

Landnamabok (Das Besiedlungsbuch). Vol. XXIII of *Thule*, Baetke (ed.). Jena, 1928.

Lucian. *A True Story*. Vol. I of *Works*. Translated by A. M. Harmon. Cambridge, Mass., 1961.

————. *Selected Satires*. Edited and translated by Lionel Casson. Chicago, 1962.

Macrobius. *Commentary on the Dream of Scipio*. Translated by William H. Stahl. New York, 1952.

Manegold of Lautenbach. *Opusculum Contra Wolfelmum Coloniensem*. Vol. CLV of *Patrologiae Cursus Completus, Series Latina*, J. P. Migne (ed.). Paris, 1880.

Mela (Pomponius Mela). *De Chorographia*. Edited by Karl Frick. Leipzig, 1880.

Maregarto, in *Denkmäler Deutschen Poesie*, K. Müllenhoff and W. Scherer (eds.). Berlin, 1892.

Minucius Felix. *Octavius*. Vol. IV of *Ante-Nicene Fathers*, Alexander Roberts and James Donaldson (eds.). New York, 1907.

————. *Octavius*. Vol. III of *Patrologiae Cursus Completus, Series Latina*, J. P. Migne (ed.). Paris, 1886.

Müllenhoff, K. and W. Scherer (eds.). *Denkmäler Deutschen Poesie und Prosa*. Berlin, 1892.

Müller, Carl (ed.). *Fragmenta Historicorum Graecorum*. Paris, 1928. 5 Vols.

Neckam, Alexander. *De Naturis Rerum Libri Duo. With the Poem of the same Author, De Laudibus Divinae Sapientiae*. Edited by Thomas Wright. London, 1863.

Nonius Marcellus. *De Conpendiosa Doctrina*. Edited by Wallace M. Lindsay. Leipzig, 1903.

Ordericus Vitalis. *Historiae Ecclesiasticae*. Paris, 1852. 5 Vols.

Orosius. *Historiarum Libri VIII*. Vol. XXXI of *Patrologiae Cursus Completus, Series Latina*, J. P. Migne (ed.). Paris, 1846.

————. *Seven Books of History Against the Pagans*. Translated by I. W. Raymond. New York, 1936.

Ovid. *Fasti*. Edited with translation and commentary by James G. Frazer. London, 1929. 5 Vols.

Paterculus. *Compendium of Roman History*. Translated by Frederick W. Shipley. New York, 1924.

Paul the Deacon. *History of the Langobards*. Translated by William Dudley Foulke. Philadelphia, 1907.

Philo. *On the Eternity of the World*, in the *Works of Philo*. Translated by F. H. Colson. Cambridge, Mass., 1941. 10 Vols.

Pindar. *Odes*. Translated by Sir John Sandys. New York, 1924.

Plato. *Dialogues*. Translated by B. Jowett. New York, 1911. 4 Vols.

Pliny the Elder. *Natural History*. Translated by H. Rackham. Cambridge, Mass., 1942. 10 Vols.

————. *Natural History*. Translated by John Bostock and H. T. Riley. London, 1887. 6 Vols.

————. *Naturalis Historia*. Edited by Gabriel Brotier. London, 1826. 11 Vols.

Plummer, Charles (ed.). *Vitae Sanctorum Hiberniae.* Oxford, 1910. 2 Vols.

Plutarch. *Lives.* Translated by Bernadotte Perrin. New York, 1919. 11 Vols.

———. *Selected Essays.* Translated by T. G. Tucker and A. O. Prickard. Oxford, 1913–18. 2 Vols.

Priscian. *Interpretatio Ex Dionysio de Orbe Situ,* in *Opera.* Edited by Augustus Krehl. Leipzig, 1819–20. 2 Vols.

Procopius of Caesarea. *History of the Wars.* Translated by H. B. Dewing. New York, 1914–40. 7 Vols.

Ptolemy. *Geography of Claudius Ptolemy.* Translated by E. L. Stevenson. New York, 1932.

Rabanus Maurus. *De Universo.* Vol. CXI of *Patrologiae Cursus Completus, Series Latina,* J. P. Migne (ed.). Paris, 1852.

Ravennatis Anonymi Cosmographia. Edited by M. Pinder and G. Parthey. Berlin, 1860.

Li Romans d'Alixandre par Lambert li Tors et Alexandre de Bernay. Edited by Heinrich Michelant. Stuttgart, 1846.

The Saga of Hacon, Hacon's Son. Translated by G. Vigfusson. London, 1894.

Saxo Grammaticus. *The First Nine Books of the Danish History of Saxo Grammaticus.* Edited by Oliver Elton and Frederick Y. Powell. London, 1894.

Seneca the Elder. *Oratorum et Rhetorum.* Edited by H. J. Müller. Leipzig, 1887.

Seneca (Sénèque). *Questions Naturelles.* Edited and translated by Paul Oltramare. Paris, 1929. 2 Vols.

Seneca. *Tragedies.* Translated by Frank J. Miller. New York, 1927. 2 Vols.

Snorre Sturlason. *Heimskringla.* Edited and translated by Erling Monsen and A. H. Smith. New York, 1932.

———. *Heimskringla.* Translated by Lee M. Hollander. New York, 1964.

Solinus. *Collectanea Rerum Memorabilium.* Edited by Theodor Mommsen. Berlin, 1895.

Staveren, Augustino van. *Auctores Mythographi Latini.* Amsterdam, 1742.

Steele, Robert. *Mediaeval Lore from Bartholomew Anglicus.* London, 1924.

Strabo. *Geography.* Translated by H. L. Jones. New York, 1917–32. 8 Vols.

Suetonius. *Lives of the Caesars.* Translated by J. C. Rolfe. New York, 1920. 2 Vols.

Tacitus. *Annals*. Translated by John Jackson. New York, 1931. 3 Vols.
————. *Dialogus; Agricola; Germania*. Translated by William Peterson. New York, 1914.
Tertullian. *Ad Nationes*. Translated by Peter Holmes. Vol. XI of *Ante-Nicene Christian Library*, Alexander Roberts and James Donaldson (eds.). Edinburgh, 1869.
————. *On the Ascetics' Mantle*. Translated by S. Thelwall. Vol. XVIII of *Ante-Nicene Christian Library*. Alexander Roberts and James Donaldson (eds.). Edinburgh, 1870.
Thomas of Britain. *The Romance of Tristram and Ysolt*. Translated by Roger S. Loomis. New York, 1951.
Vincent of Beauvais. *Speculum Naturale*. Venetijs, 1494.
Virgil. *Opera*. Edited by John Covington and Henry Nettleship. London, 1881. 3 Vols.
Vita Prima Sancti Brendani, in *Vitae Sanctorum Hiberniae*. Edited by Charles Plummer. Oxford, 1910. 2 Vols.
Vita Sancti Albei, in *Vitae Sanctorum Hiberniae*. Edited by Charles Plummer. Oxford, 1910. 2 Vols.
Voyage of Bran, Son of Febal. Edited and translated by Kuno Meyer with an essay by Alfred Nutt. London, 1895. 2 Vols.
Voyage of Mael Duin. Edited and translated by Whitley Stokes. In *Revue Celtique*, IX (1888), 447–95, and *Revue Celtique*, X (1889), 50–95.
Voyage of Snedgus and MacRiagla. Edited and translated by Whitley Stokes. In *Revue Celtique*, IX (1888), 14–25.
Voyage of the Hui Corra. Edited and translated by Whitley Stokes. In *Revue Celtique*, XIV (1893), 22–69.
Warmington, E. H. *Greek Geography*. New York: E. P. Dutton, 1934.
William of Conches. *De Philosophia Mundi*. Vol. CLXXII of *Patrologiae Cursus Completus, Series Latina*, J. P. Migne (ed.). Paris, 1895.

II SECONDARY SOURCES

Ahlman, Hans W. "Rediscovering Vinland," a review of Helge Ingstad, *Vesterveg til Vinland*. Translated from *Svenska Dagbladet* (Stockholm) in *Atlas* (March, 1966), 187–90.
Ashe, Geoffrey. *Land to the West*. New York, 1962.
Avezac-Macaya, M. A. P. d'. *Le Ravennate et son Exposé Cosmographique*. Rouen, 1888.
Babcock, William H. *Early Norse Visits to North America*. Vol. LIX

of *Smithsonian Miscellaneous Collections,* no. 19. Washington, 1913.

————. *Legendary Islands of the Atlantic.* New York, 1922.

————. "St Brendan's Islands," *Geographical Review* (July, 1919).

Bagrow, Leo. *Die Geschichte der Kartographie.* Berlin, 1951.

————. "Eskimo Maps," *Imago Mundi,* V (1948), 92.

————. *History of Cartography.* Revised and enlarged by R. A. Skelton. London, 1964.

Ballesteros, A. (ed.). *Historia de América.* Buenos Aires, 1947–48. 25 Vols.

Batalha-Reis, J. "The Supposed Discovery of South America before 1448, and the Critical Methods of the Historians of Geographical Discovery," *Geographical Journal,* IX (1897), 185–210.

Beazley, C. R. *Dawn of Modern Geography.* London, 1897–1906. 3 Vols.

Bennett, Josephine Waters. "Britain among the Fortunate Isles," *Studies in Philology,* LIII (1956), 114–40.

Birket-Smith, Kaj. *The Eskimos.* London, 1959.

Boak, Arthur E. R. *Manpower Shortage and the Fall of the Roman Empire in the West.* Ann Arbor, 1955.

Boland, Charles M. *They All Discovered America.* New York, 1961.

Brehaut, Ernest. *An Encyclopaedist of the Dark Ages, Isidore of Seville.* New York, 1912.

Bright, James W. *Anglo-Saxon Reader.* Revised by James R. Hulbert. New York, 1947.

Brögger, A. W. and Haakon Shetelig. *The Viking Ships, Their Ancestry and Evolution.* Los Angeles, 1953.

Brown, Arthur C. L. "The Wonderful Flower that came to St. Brendan, *Manly Anniversary Studies in Language and Literature.* Chicago, 1923. pp. 295–99.

Brown, Lloyd A. *The Story of Maps.* Boston, 1949.

Burton, Harry E. *Discovery of the Ancient World.* London, 1932.

Carson, Rachel L. *The Sea Around Us.* New York, 1951.

Carter, G. F. "Archaeological Maize in West Africa," *Man,* XCV (May, 1964), 85–86.

Cary, M. and E. H. Warmington. *The Ancient Explorers.* London, 1929.

Cassidy, Vincent H. deP. "The Location of Ginnunga-gap," *Scandinavian Studies.* Edited by Carl F. Bayerschmidt and Erik J. Friis for the American-Scandinavian Foundation. Seattle, 1965. pp. 27–38.

————. "The Voyage of an Island," *Speculum,* XXXVIII (1963), 595–602.

Catlin, George. *North American Indians.* Edinburgh, 1926. 2 Vols.

Châtillon, Jean. "Le *Didascalicon* de Hugues de Saint-Victor," *Journal of World History*, IX (1966), 539–52.

Clapham, Sir John. *A Concise Economic History of Britain*. London, 1949.

Collinder, Per. *A History of Marine Navigation*. Translated by Maurice Michael. New York, 1955.

Compton, Carl B. "Maize," *The InterAmerican*, XII, no. 8 (November, 1965).

Crone, G. R. "How Authentic is the 'Vinland Map,'" *Encounter*, XXVI (February, 1966), 75–78.

———. "The Vinland Map Geographically Considered," *Geographical Journal*, CXXXII (March, 1966), 75–80.

Cross, Tom Peete. "The Passing of Arthur," *Manly Anniversary Studies in Language and Literature*. Chicago, 1923. pp. 284–94.

de Camp, L. Sprague. *Lost Continents*. New York, 1954.

de Gandillac, Maurice. "Encyclopédies Pré-Médiévales et Médiévales," *Journal of World History*, IX (1966), 483–518.

de Latil, Pierre and Jean Rivoire. *Man and the Underwater World*. New York, 1956.

Ebbinghaus, Ernst A. "A Note on the Meregarto," *Journal of English and German Philology*, LXIV (1965), 232–33.

Einarsson, Stefán. "Bjólfur and Grendill in Iceland," *Modern Language Notes*, LXXI (1956), 79–81.

Ekwall, Eilert. *Concise Oxford Dictionary of English Place Names*. Oxford, 1936.

Eliade, Mircea. *Patterns in Comparative Religion*. New York, 1963.

Fontaine, Jacques. "Isidore de Séville et la mutation de l' Encyclopédisme Antique," *Journal of World History*, IX (1966), 519–38.

Fried, Jacob. *A Survey of the Aboriginal Populations of Quebec and Labrador*. Montreal, 1955.

Frobenius, Leo. *The Voice of Africa*. London, 1913. 2 Vols.

Gaffarel, Paul. *Les Voyages de Saint-Brandan et des Papoe dans l'Atlantique au Moyen Age*. Extrait du *Bulletin de La Société de Géographie de Rochefort*, 1880–81.

Galanopoulos, Angelos C. "Letters to the Science Editor," *Saturday Review*, XLIX (December, 1966), 93; XLX (April, 1967), 56.

Gatty, Harold. *Nature Is Your Guide*. New York, 1958.

———. *The Raft Book, Lore of the Sea and Sky*. New York, 1943.

Gjerset, Knut. *History of the Norwegian People*. New York, 1915.

Glynn, Frank. "A New Prehistoric Settlement Pattern." Abstract of Paper—November 7, 1959: Eastern States Archaeological Federation.

Goldstein, Thomas E. "Conceptual Patterns Underlying the Vinland Map," *Renaissance News*, XIX (1966), 321–31.

Goodwin, William B. *The Ruins of Great Ireland in New England.* Boston, 1946.

——. *The Truth About Leif Ericsson and the Greenland Voyages.* Boston, 1941.

Grenfell, Sir Wilfred. *The Romance of Labrador.* New York, 1934.

Grimal, Pierre. "Encyclopédies Antiques," *Journal of World History,* IX (1966), 459–82.

Gründel, Johannes. "L'oeuvre encyclopédique de Raoul Ardent: *Le Speculum Universale," Journal of World History,* IX (1966), 553–70.

Hapgood, Charles. *Maps of the Ancient Sea Kings.* New York, 1966.

——. "Mystery at North Salem," *New Hampshire Town Crier* (June 22, 1961), 3–4, 9.

Hawkins, Gerald S. *Stonehenge Decoded.* New York, 1965.

Hencken, Hugh. "The 'Irish Monastery' at North Salem, New Hampshire," *New England Quarterly,* XII (1939), 429–42.

Hennessy, William G. "North Salem Mystery," *New Hampshire Profiles,* August, 1952.

Hermannsson, Halldór. *Bibliography of the Sagas of the Kings of Norway and Related Sagas and Tales.* Vol. III of *Islandica.* Ithaca, 1910.

——. *The Cartography of Iceland.* Vol. XXI of *Islandica.* Ithaca, 1931.

——. *The Problem of Wineland,* Vol. XXV of *Islandica.* Ithaca, 1936.

——. *Two Icelandic Cartographers.* Vol. XVII of *Islandica.* Ithaca, 1926.

Hill, Evan. "The North Salem Mystery," *Saturday Evening Post* (August 8, 1959), 32 ff.

Hill, J. H. and L. L. "L'allégorie chrétienne dans les récits relatifs au Wineland," *Le Moyen Âge,* LXVI (1960), 65–83.

Hobbs, William H. "Zeno and the Cartography of Greenland," *Imago Mundi,* VI (1949), 15–19.

Hodnett, Mona P. "The Sea in Roman Poetry," *Classical Journal,* XV (1919–20), 67–82.

Holand, Hjalmar R. *Explorations in America Before Columbus.* New York, 1958.

Holmes, T. Rice. "Could Ancient Ships Work to Windward?," *Classical Quarterly,* III (1909), 26–39.

Hornell, Jame. *British Coracles and Irish Curraghs.* London, 1938.

Hovgaard, William. *The Voyages of the Norsemen to America.* New York, 1914.

Hui-Lin Li. "Mu-Lan-Pi: A Case for Pre-Columbian Transatlantic

Travel by Arab Ships," *Harvard Journal of Asiatic Studies*, XXIII (1961), 114–26.

Hyde, Walter W. *Ancient Greek Mariners*. New York, 1947.

"Important Discoveries in Quebec," *N.E.A.R.A. Newsletter*, II, no. 1 (March, 1967), 6–7.

Ingstad, Helge. *Land Under the Pole Star*. New York, 1966.

———. "Vinland Ruins Prove Vikings Found the New World," *National Geographic*, XXVI (1964), 708–34.

Jeffreys, M. D. W. "Maize and the Ambiguity in Columbus' Letter," *Anthropological Journal of Canada*, III, no. 4 (1965), 2–11.

Jones, Charles W. *Bedae Pseudepigrapha: Scientific Writings Falsely Attributed to Bede*. Ithaca, 1939.

Jones, Gwyn. *The Norse Atlantic Saga*. London, 1964.

———. "The Vikings." *New York Review of Books*, VIII (April 6, 1967), 32–35.

Kenney, James F. *The Sources for the Early History of Ireland: Ecclesiastical*. New York, 1929.

Kimble, George H. T. *Geography in the Middle Ages*. London, 1938.

Laistner, M. L. W. *Thought and Letters in Western Europe, A.D. 500–900*. London, 1931.

Lear, John. "The Volcano that Shaped the Western World," *Saturday Review*, XLIX (November 5, 1966), 57–66.

———. "What Did the Norsemen Discover?," *Saturday Review* (November 6, 1965), 49–52.

Leip, Hans. *The River in the Sea*. New York, 1958.

Leithäuser, Joachim G. *Mappae Mundi*. Berlin, 1958.

Lemoine, Michel. "L'oeuvre encyclopédique de Vincent de Beauvias," *Journal of World History*, IX (1966), 571–79.

Lethbridge, T. C. *Boats and Boatmen*. New York, 1952.

———. *Herdsmen and Hermits*. Cambridge, 1950.

———. *Merlin's Island, Essays on Britain in the Dark Ages*. London, 1948.

Lewis, Archibald R. *The Northern Seas: Shipping and Commerce in Northern Europe A.D. 300–1100*. Princeton, 1958.

Magnusson, Magnus and Hermann Palsson. *The Vinland Sagas*. New York, 1966.

Mallery, Arlington H. *Lost America*. Columbus, Ohio, 1951.

Malone, Kemp. "King Alfred's North, a Study in Mediaeval Geography," *Speculum*, V (1930), 139–67.

———. "On King Alfred's Geographical Treatise," *Speculum*, VIII (1933), 67–78.

Manitius, M. *Geschichte der Lateinischen Literatur des Mittelalters*. Munich, 1931. 3 Vols.

Marcus, G. J. "Factors in Early Celtic Navigation," *Études Celtiques*, VI (1953–54), 312–27.

Marston, Thomas E. "The Vinland Map," *Encounter*, XXVI (June, 1966), 93.

Michaud-Quantin, Pierre. "Les petites encyclopédies du XIIIᵉ Siècle," *Journal of World History*, IX (1966), 580–95.

Miller, Maynard M. "Floating Islands," *Natural History*, LXV (1956), 233–39, 274–76.

Mowat, Farley. *Westviking*. Boston, 1965.

Nansen, Fridtjof. *In Northern Mists*. Translated by Arthur G. Chater. London, 1911. 2 vols.

Nitze, William A. "Erec and the Joy of the Court," *Speculum*, XXIX (1954), 691–701.

Nordenskiöld, A. E. *Facsimile Atlas to the Early History of Cartography*. Stockholm, 1889.

Norlund, Poul. *Viking Settlers in Greenland*. London, 1936.

"Note on Avienus," *Classical Journal*, II (1812), 297.

Ogilvy, J. D. A. *Books known to Anglo-Latin Writers from Aldhelm to Alcium* (670–804). Cambridge, Mass., 1936.

Oleson, T. J. *Early Voyages and Northern Approaches*. London, 1964.

————. *The Norsemen in America*. Ottawa, 1963.

————. "The Vikings in America: A Critical Bibliography," *Canadian Historical Review*, XXXVI (1955), 166–73.

Olsen, Olaf. "The Viking Ships from Roskilde Fjord," *American Scandinavian Review*, LII (1964), 24–36.

Olson, Ted. "Implausible Island," *Saturday Review* (September, 1965), 54–55.

Oschinsky, Lawrence. *The Most Ancient Eskimos*. Ottawa, 1964.

Outhwaite, Leonard. *The Atlantic, A History of an Ocean*. New York, 1957.

Oxenstierna, Eric. *The Norsemen*. Translated by Catherine Hutter. New York, 1965.

————. "The Vikings," *Scientific American*, CCXVI (May, 1967), 66–78.

Parry, J. H. "The Vinland Story," *Perspectives in American History*, I (1967), 417–33.

Piggott, Stuart. *Ancient Europe From the Beginnings of Agriculture to Classical Antiquity*. Chicago, 1965.

Pittenger, Norman W. "Christianity and the Man on Mars," *Christian Century*, LXXIII (1956), 747–48.

Plummer, Charles. "Some New Light on the Brendan Legend," *Zeitschrift für Celtische Philologie*, V (1905), 124–41.

Pohl, Frederick J. *Atlantic Crossings Before Columbus*. New York, 1961.

————. "Leif Erickson's Campsite in Vinland," *American Scandinavian Review*, LIV, no. 1 (1966), 25–29.

————. *The Viking Explorers*. New York, 1966.

Richey, M. W. "The Vinland Map," *Journal of the Institute of Navigation*, XIX (January, 1966), 124–25.

Rothovius, Andrew E. "The Strange Stone Structures of North Salem, New Hampshire," *Anthropological Journal of Canada*, I (1963), 19–24.

————. "A Possible Megalithic Settlement Complex at North Salem, New Hampshire," *The Bulletin*, XXVII (1963), 2–10.

Sanz, Carlos. "Un mapa del mundo verdaderamente importante en la famosa Universidad de Yale," *Boletín de la Real Sociedad Geografica*, CII (1966).

Sarton, George. *Introduction to the History of Science*. Washington, D.C., 1927–31. 2 Vols.

Sawyer, P. H. *The Age of the Vikings*. New York, 1962.

Simpson, W. Douglas. *The Historical Saint Columba*. London, 1963.

Skelton, R. A. *The European Image of Mapping of America A.D. 1000–1600*. Minneapolis, 1965.

————. "Interpreting the Vinland Map," *Encounter*, XXVI (April, 1966), 92–93.

————, Thomas E. Marston, and George D. Painter. *The Vinland Map and the Tartar Relation*. New Haven, Conn., 1965.

Stahl, William H. "To A Better Understanding of Martianus Capella," *Speculum*, XL (1965), 102–15.

Stanley, E. G. "Old English Poetic Diction and the Interpretation of *The Wanderer*, *The Seafarer* and *The Penitent's Prayer*," *Anglia*, LXXIII (1956), 413–66.

Steenberghen, Fernand van. *Aristotle in the West*. Louvain, 1955.

Stefansson, Vilhjalmur. *Great Adventures and Explorations*. New York, 1952.

————. *Greenland*. New York, 1942.

————. *My Life with the Eskimos*. New York, 1913.

————. *Ultima Thule*. New York, 1940.

Steinman, Marion. "Leif Ericsson and His Relations," *Life*, LXIII (September 15, 1967), 53–64.

Stone, Robert and Osborne. "Further Progress: Excavation of a Strange Well at Mystery Hill, N. Salem, New Hampshire," *The New Hampshire Archaeologist*, XII (1963).

Storm, Gustav. "Ginnungagap i Mythologien og i Geografien," *Arkiv för Nordisk Filologi*, VI (1890) 340–50.

Swanton, John R. *The Wineland Voyages*. Vol. CVII of *Smithsonian Miscellaneous Collections*, no. 12. Washington, D.C., 1947.

Taylor, Eva G. R. *The Haven-finding Art: A History of Navigation from Odysseus to Captain Cook.* London, 1958.

———, and M. W. Richey. *The Geometrical Seaman.* London, 1962.

Thalbitzer, William. *Two Runic Stones, from Greenland and Minnesota.* Vol. CXVI of *Smithsonian Miscellaneous Collections,* no. 3 (1950–51), 1–71.

Thomson, J. Oliver. *History of Ancient Geography.* London, 1948.

Thorne, Samuel. "Record of a Visit from the Vikings," *Saturday Review* (October, 1966), 46–48.

Thoroddsen, Thorvald. *Geschichte der Isländischen Geographie.* Leipzig, 1897–98. 2 Vols.

Thrall, William F. "Clerical Sea Pilgrimages and the *Imrama*," *Manly Anniversary Studies.* Chicago, 1923. pp. 276–83.

Tooley, R. V. *Maps and Mapmakers.* London, 1952.

Toussaint, Auguste. *History of the Indian Ocean.* Translated by June Guicharnaud. London, 1961.

Tozer, H. T. *A History of Ancient Geography.* Second edition with additional notes by M. Cary. London, 1935.

Uhden, Richard. "Die antiken Grundlagen de mittelalterlichen Seekarten," *Imago Mundi,* I (1935), 1–19.

Vendryes, J. "Manannan MacLir," *Études Celtiques,* VI (1953–54), 239–54.

Wallace, W. S. "Literature Relating to the Norse Voyages to America," *Canadian Historical Review,* XX (1939), 8–16.

Whitaker, Ian. "The Scottish Kayaks and the Finn-men," *Antiquity,* XXVIII (1954), 99–104.

Whitelock, Dorothy. "The Interpretation of *The Seafarer*," in *Early Cultures of Northwest Europe: H. M. Chadwick Memorial Studies,* Sir Cyril Fox and Bruce Dickins (eds.). London, 1950. pp. 259–72.

Wiener, Leo. *Africa and the Discovery of America.* Philadelphia, 1920–22. 3 vols.

Winter, Heinrich. "The Origin of the Sea Chart," *Imago Mundi,* VIII (1951), 39–44.

———. "The True Position of Hermann Wagner in the Controversy of the Compass Chart," *Imago Mundi,* V (1948), 21–26.

Wolfe, Michael. "Norse Archaeology in Greenland Since World War Two," *American Scandinavian Review,* XLIX (1961), 380–92.

Wright, John Kirtland. *The Geographical Lore of the Time of the Crusades.* New York, 1925.

Young, Jean. "Some Icelandic Traditions Showing Traces of Irish Influence," *Études Celtiques,* II (1937), 118–26.

Index

Abelard, Peter: says earth sphere in water, 119, 158–59; cited, 119

Abu'l-Hasan 'Ali Ibn Sa'id: re Greenland, 136

abyss: Isidore re, 64, 162; as cause of tides, 108, 161; as source of all water, 120

Adalbert, Archbishop of Bremen: as informant of Adam of Bremen, 107

Adamnan: writes biography of Columba, 91, 167; and references to seafaring, 91–92; cited, 91, 92

Adam of Bremen: re Greenland, 35, 106, 167; re Norse discoveries, 105–109, 165; and scholastic sources, 105; world view of, 105, 158; re Iceland, 105–106; re Harald Hardrada, 106; re Frisian nobles, 107–108; re tides, 107, 108; possible Irish sources of, 110; mentioned, 111, 112, 122–23; cited, 36, 105, 106, 107, 108

Adelard of Bath: influenced by Arabic scholarship, 115; treatise of on astrolabe, 115; ideas of re ocean in *Quaestiones Naturales*, 115–16, 161; mentioned, 155, 162; cited, 115

Aegean Sea, 27

Aelian: re transoceanic land, 28; acceptance of Atlantis, 29; cited, 28, 29

Aelfric, Abbot of St. Albans: relies on Basil's *Hexaemeron*, 47

Aelfric, Archbishop of Canterbury: may be Aelfric of St. Albans, 47

Aethicus of Istria: as author of cos-

mography, 61; re north Atlantic islands, 61; re Alexander the Great on sea bottom, 62; cited, 62

Africa: west coast of explored by Hanno, 4; circumnavigation of, 6, 21; Roman exploration of west coast of, 8; and supposed link with India, 21; connected with Vinland, 122; mentioned, 25, 26n, 28, 30, 38, 40, 41, 45, 53, 54, 55, 65, 71, 72, 116, 117, 151–52, 154, 168, 169

African islands, 124

Agricola (Roman General): sails north of Britain, 12

Ailbe, St.: as monkish navigator, 86; seeks Thule, 87; mentioned, 87, 150, 166

Albania, 136–39. *See* Whiteman's land

Albertus Magnus, St., 156, 160

Albion: as name of Britain, 32

Albi world map, 70

Albinovanus. *See* Pedo Albinovanus

Alebrand: Archbishop of Bremen, 107, 108

Alexander the Great: and interest in maritime exploration, 6n; medieval romances re, 152; submarine explorations of, 62, 152; mentioned, 6, 55

Alexandria, 28, 38

Alfred the Great: translates Orosius' *History*, 53, 59, 73; as scholar-translator, 69; additions of to Boethius' *Consolation of Philosophy*, 69; receives Irish pilgrims, 98; opposes Norse, 99–100; begins